Leckie✗Leckie

Scotland's leading educational publishers

D0198369

National 5
GEOGRAPHY
SUCCESS GUIDE

N5 GEOGRAPHY SUCCESS GUIDE

*Rob Hands, Alison Hughes,
Samantha Peck*

© 2013 Leckie & Leckie Ltd
Cover © ink-tank and associates/Muzhik

001/04102013

10 9 8 7 6 5 4 3 2 1

ISBN 9780007504930

Published by
Leckie & Leckie Ltd
An imprint of HarperCollins*Publishers*
Westerhill Road, Bishopbriggs, Glasgow, G64 2QT
T: 0844 576 8126   F: 0844 576 8131
leckieandleckie@harpercollins.co.uk   www.leckieandleckie.co.uk

Special thanks to
Donna Cole (copyedit)
Louise Robb (proofread)
Q2A Bill Smith (layout and illustrations)
Ian Geddes (content review)
Rob Hands (illustrations)

Printed in Italy by Lego S.P.A.

A CIP Catalogue record for this book is available from the British Library.

Acknowledgements

We would like to thank the following for permission to reproduce their material:
Photograph of Glenshee Ski Centre on page 34 © Brendan Howard/Shutterstock.com; Photograph of Weston-Super-Mare beach on page 43 © Mike Charles/Shutterstock.com; Photograph of Masai family on page 50 © Birute Vijeikiene/Shutterstock.com; Photograph of London 2012 Olympics on page 60 © pcruciatti/Shutterstock.com; Photograph of damage caused by Hurricane Sandy on page 75 © Leonard Zhukovsky / Shutterstock.com; Photograph of oil spill on page 74 © National Geographic/Getty Images; Photograph of doctors' surgery in Kenya on page 101 © spirit of america/Shutterstock.com; Photograph of doctors' surgery in the UK on page 106 © Dmitry Berkut/Shutterstock.com

All other images from Shutterstock or Thinkstock.

OS Maps
Ordnance Survey ® map data licensed with the permission of the Controller of Her Majesty's Stationery Office.
© Crown copyright. Licence number 100018598.

Whilst every effort has been made to trace the copyright holders, in cases where this has been unsuccessful, or if any have inadvertently been overlooked, the Publishers would gladly receive any information enabling them to rectify any error or omission at the first opportunity.

Contents

The course and the exam

Units and Added Value Unit

In the N5 Geography course you will study a wide variety of topics, which will be broken down into three units: Physical Environments, Human Environments and Global Issues.

You will also complete an Added Value Unit, which may have taken the form of a project, a presentation, a field study or a report. Throughout this book you will find some suggestions of what you could do to complete this component of the N5 Geography Award.

Key skills in Geography include being able to use a range of numerical and graphical information in the context of physical, human and global geographical issues, drawing on detailed knowledge and understanding of a significant global geographical issue and using skills to research in depth a specific line of enquiry. You should also familiarise yourself with OS maps – a key tool for Geography students in learning about the world.

Unit 1: Physical Environments

In this unit you study weather and climate, and then choose between rivers and limestone, or glaciation and coasts. Alternatively, you may have studied all four topics in preparation for moving onto Higher Geography at a later date. You will study the key processes, the formation of features and a case study of a named coastal area, such as the Dorset Coast or the Pembrokshire Coast, or upland area, such as the Cairngorms or the Lake District, and then apply this to examination questions.

In the exam you will have a choice of questions for Physical Environments. You should attempt *either* Question 1 or Question 2 *and* Questions 3, 4 and 5. This will account for 20 marks.

Fig i. A limestone pavement in Malham

Unit 2: Human Environments

In this unit you will study contrasts between developed and developing countries, in both urban and rural areas. Again you should have named case study material, having looked at specific named countries and cities from across the globe. You will also learn about world population and migration and should be able to answer questions 6, 7 and 8 of the exam paper. This too will account for 20 marks.

Fig ii. A Brazilian favela

Unit 3: Human Global Issues

This topic is set on a global scale so you can use case studies from any country in the world. You should study at least two global issues and must be able to answer questions in the exam from two of the following topics, again accounting for 20 marks:

- Climate change
- Impact of human activity on the natural environment
- Environmental hazards
- Trade and globalisation
- Tourism
- Development and health

Fig iii. A crowded tourist beach

Added value project ideas

A number of project ideas are included in this book as well as one or two more detailed guides to help you work on your own projects and investigations. Here are some suggestions that will help you to design your own project.

1. Carry out a study in one of the key sectors of a city you live in or know well, e.g. investigate changes in Edinburgh's central business district (C.B.D.).

   - Gather your data, process it, present it, analyse it.
   - Key skills required here include: land use mapping, surveys (traffic, pedestrians, building height), questionnaires, data processing, data analysis.
   - If you can carry out field work locally, you could use secondary data to compare how the city/town has changed over time. Use old OS maps and Google Earth to gather data.

Fig iv. Princes Street, Edinburgh

2. Physical landscape projects might involve mapping features seen in the field, drawing and annotating field sketches, drawing cross sections and explanatory diagrams, creating maps using Google satellite images as a base. Projects should try to explain how features form. Possible topics that might be investigated are:

   - Rivers – What changes would you find along a river from source to mouth? How does the bed load change along a river's course? What changes in land use are there along a river's course?
   - Limestone landscapes – Investigation into land use conflicts within the Yorkshire Dales National Park. An investigation into the advantages and disadvantages of a proposed development with the National Park, e.g. a quarry.
   - Coasts – Investigation into the possible impact of a proposed coastal development and how this would affect the natural processes at work along the coastline. What are the advantages and disadvantages of a new coastal protection scheme?

3. Global issues can be investigated using a study question or a series of questions.

   - What will the impact of a wind farm be on the local area?
   - An environmental issue for and against: what are the merits of both sides of a debate and what conclusion do you arrive at?
   - Why should more areas of Scotland be designated as national parks?
   - Why do people object to developments in an environmentally sensitive area? (Local, UK, European Union (EU) or global.)

4. What are the effects of tourism on an area? Visitor survey, Internet research, relating the area to the Butler Model, environmental impact survey, debate.

5. A case study of a disease and how it affects people. Mapping distributions, diagrams defining transmission and environmental factors involved, economic and social effects, research, prevention and cure.

6. A comparison of a developed and developing country using statistical information from library and Internet sources.

7. A study of the impact of a development, e.g. hydroelectric power (HEP) scheme, industrial development on a fragile environment such as in the Tundra or in the Equatorial Rainforest.

8. A comparison of the trading patterns of particular developed and developing countries.

Fig v. Deforestation in the Amazon rainforest

Britain's weather

High and low pressure

Britain's weather is dominated by **Atlantic low pressure systems** (depressions or cyclones) that sweep across the British Isles from west to east. These bring a mix of warm **tropical maritime** air and cold **polar maritime** air. Cold air is denser so it moves more quickly and undercuts warmer air at the rear of the depression, or blocks its movement in at the leading edge of this feature (see Fig 1.1).

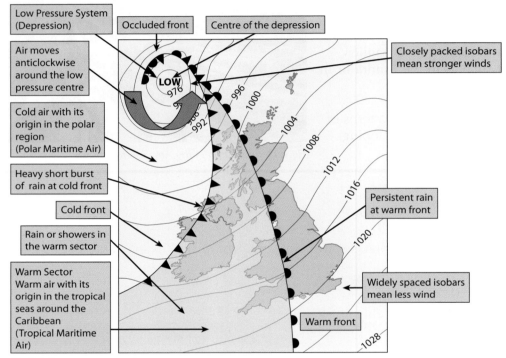

Low Pressure System (Depression)

Occluded front

Centre of the depression

Closely packed isobars mean stronger winds

Air moves anticlockwise around the low pressure centre

Cold air with its origin in the polar region (Polar Maritime Air)

Heavy short burst of rain at cold front

Cold front

Rain or showers in the warm sector

Warm Sector
Warm air with its origin in the tropical seas around the Caribbean (Tropical Maritime Air)

Persistent rain at warm front

Widely spaced isobars mean less wind

Warm front

Fig 1.1 Low pressure system

High pressure air Anti-Cyclone

HIGH

Wind moves clockwise around a high pressure

Cold frosty air in winter

Hot and dry in summer

Widely space isobars – light winds

Fig 1.2 High pressure system

What are weather fronts?

An air mass is a large body of air that has similar moisture, density and temperature characteristics. Air masses with different temperature, moisture and pressure characteristics tied up in depressions do not mix easily. A front is the boundary separating two air masses.

Fig 1.3 Where air masses meet

A warm front is where warm air contacts cold air. The contact zone is at ground level and reaches high above, up into the atmosphere. The diagram (Fig 1.3) demonstrates how at the warm front the warm sector is being forced to rise over the cold air in front of it. As it rises, it cools and condenses and forms clouds, leading to persistent rainfall on the ground. Behind the front, the warm sector is being squeezed and forced to rise by the heavier dense cold air driving in behind it. Here, showers of rain may occur.

A cold front is where cold air contacts warm air. At the cold front, heavy cloud is created by the associated uplift of warm air and a burst of heavy rain is likely. Behind the cold front, the polar maritime cold air is more stable and drier colder conditions might be expected. If the warm sector loses contact with the ground, the front becomes an **occluded** front, which will likely deliver heavy rain.

On weather maps, weather systems can be identified, along with their fronts and pressure readings. Atmospheric pressure is shown on the maps using contour-like **isobars.** These show pressure in **millibars** (mb) at intervals of 4 mb. Wind direction can be interpreted from the isobar pattern on a map. Winds blow **anti-clockwise** around low pressure systems just off parallel to the isobars in towards the centre of the low pressure system. Where isobars are close together this indicates a steep pressure gradient and therefore strong winds. Widely spaced isobars such as in Fig 1.2 mean little wind is being experienced on the ground.

Quick Test

1. What air masses are typically mixed in an Atlantic depression?
2. Which moves the quickest in a depression warm air or cold air?
3. What is a front?
4. What is created if the warm sector leaves the ground?
5. If winds move anti-clockwise around low pressure systems, which way do they move around a high pressure system?

The passage of a depression over Britain

Cyclonic systems (depressions and fronts) bring a sequence of weather events as they pass over Britain. Standing at any point on the ground, a weather watcher will see the sequence as follows: Study Fig 1.1

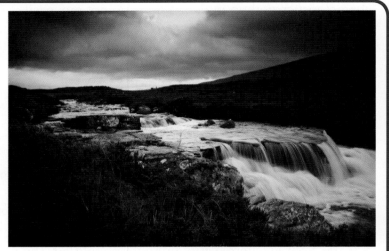

Fig 1.4 Dense cloud cover during a depression

Stage 1: The depression approaches, moving west to east.

Weather conditions: In the forward cold sector the weather is bright and sunny. High-level cloud (cirrus and cirro-stratus) begins to develop. A halo around the moon or sun can be observed as the warm front approaches.

Wind: Winds are light and south-westerly but begin to increase in strength.

Stage 2: The warm front arrives.

Weather conditions: At the warm front, there are long periods of persistent rain. There is dense cloud cover (stratus or strato-cumulus clouds) that gives full sky cover.

Wind: Wind speeds increase and the wind changes direction at the front, switching to westerly. Wind speed increases and may reach storm- or gale-force in a typical storm.

Stage 3: The warm sector.

Weather conditions: The rain eases and temperatures rise as the warm air passes over. It may become showery or drizzly.

Wind: Winds remain strong and westerly.

Stage 4: The cold front arrives.

Weather conditions: There is a heavy burst of rain for a short time as the steep front passes. Temperature drops as the cold air follows behind its front.

Wind: Winds back around from the north-west as the front passes, bringing in colder air.

Stage 5: Behind the cold front.

Weather conditions: The polar maritime or Arctic air is colder and stable so produces cold dry conditions with decreasing cloud (cumulus) as the weather clears up.

Wind: Winds from the north-west are blustery at first but wind speed decreases as the front moves away. Calmer conditions follow.

High pressure systems: anticyclones

Fig 1.5 Edinburgh in a high pressure system

High pressure systems are called anticyclones. They are less common in Britain but can build to bring long periods of stable weather. In summer, high pressure brings hot, dry conditions with low wind speeds while winter days are often cold and frosty, and fog and ice may develop. Night time temperatures are particularly low, and bright sunny winter days may stay below freezing. Easterly winds bring snow to eastern Britain in winter.

EXAM TIP

The best way to learn about weather is to follow weather forecasts on TV and the Internet. Search for the Met Office, BBC Weather Service or the Mountain Weather Information Service.

DID YOU KNOW?

The lowest recorded temperature in Scotland was –27°, first recorded in Braemar in 1982 and then again in the Highlands in 2010.

Weather plots

On complex weather maps and synoptic charts, codes are used to plot the weather at a weather station (for example at an airport). These provide a summary of the weather at a glance provided that you can work out the key that cracks the code.

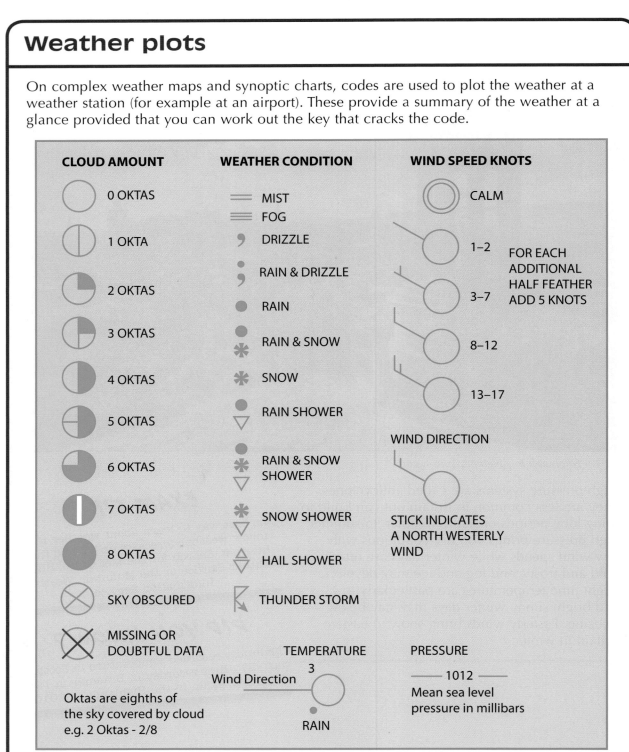

Fig 1.6 Synoptic chart symbols

Activity

1. Look at the three weather plots below and summarise the weather being experienced at each, using the weather plot symbols above to help you.

2. Draw weather plots showing the following weather conditions:

   a. The wind is northerly, blowing at 15 knots. The temperature is –6°C and there are snow showers. There are 7 oktas of cloud.

   b. The sky is obscured. There is fog. There is a light wind blowing from the south-east at 2 knots. The temperature is 4°C.

   c. The wind is south-westerly blowing at 40 knots. The sky is completely covered by cloud and there is rain and drizzle.

3. Study the weather map to the right.

   a. Summarise the weather at each of the weather stations a, b, e and g.

   b. Describe the weather at station h and explain why the weather is like that.

WEATHER CHART

BRITISH ISLES February 1st 2011 (1300hrs)

Fig 1.8 Weather map of the UK

0   100 km

Quick Test

1. In which direction do most low pressure systems (depressions) cross the British Isles? Choose from east to west; north to south; south-east to north-west; or west to east.

2. What would a weather observer notice as the cold front arrives?

3. What is another name for a high pressure system?

4. What weather conditions are likely with a high pressure system over Scotland in winter?

Factors affecting climate and weather in the UK

The climate and weather of a place depends on a number of factors:

1. Latitude

   - Temperatures generally decrease with distance from the Equator – this is because of the Earth's tilt and its curvature.
   - At the Equator, the sun is at a high angle at midday at all times of the year – the sun's heating effect is at its greatest.
   - As you move from the Equator to the poles, the angle of the midday sun gets lower and the sun's heating effect gets less as it is spread over a greater area.

2. Relief/altitude

   - Local relief (the shape of the land) and the height (altitude) are important in determining the local climate.
   - Temperatures decrease by 1°C for every 100 metres gained in height. Upland areas are therefore cooler than surrounding lowlands.
   - Wind speeds increase as altitude increases.

3. Aspect

   - Aspect refers to the direction that slopes are facing. In the northern hemisphere, south-facing slopes are warm as they face the sun. North-facing slopes are shaded and are therefore cooler: frost and snow lie longer in the winter and the slope does not get so hot in summer.
   - Slopes alter the angle at which the sun's rays hit the ground.
   - Land use can be affected by aspect – sunny south-facing slopes are better for agriculture.

4. Distance from the sea

   - Land and sea differ in their ability to absorb, transfer and reflect heat.
   - The sea can absorb heat to a greater depth (10 metres) than the land. This means it takes longer to heat up and longer to cool down.
   - Places closer to the sea have milder winters and cooler summers. Oceans act as 'thermal reservoirs' (hot water bottles to us!) and so coastal areas rarely suffer from frost and heavy snowfall and have a lower annual range of temperature than inland areas.

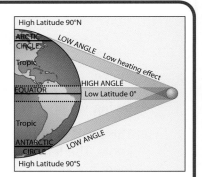
Fig 1.9 The effects of latitude

Fig 1.10 The effects of relief

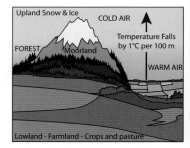
Fig 1.11 The effects of aspect

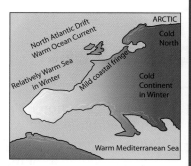
Fig 1.12 The effects of distance from the sea

Air masses

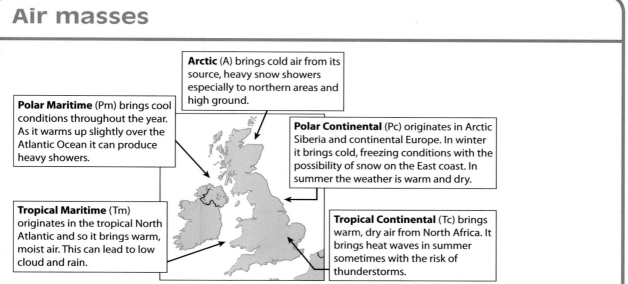

Polar Maritime (Pm) brings cool conditions throughout the year. As it warms up slightly over the Atlantic Ocean it can produce heavy showers.

Arctic (A) brings cold air from its source, heavy snow showers especially to northern areas and high ground.

Polar Continental (Pc) originates in Arctic Siberia and continental Europe. In winter it brings cold, freezing conditions with the possibility of snow on the East coast. In summer the weather is warm and dry.

Tropical Maritime (Tm) originates in the tropical North Atlantic and so it brings warm, moist air. This can lead to low cloud and rain.

Tropical Continental (Tc) brings warm, dry air from North Africa. It brings heat waves in summer sometimes with the risk of thunderstorms.

Fig 1.13 Air masses affecting the British Isles

The weather in the UK is directly affected by the winds that blow over it. These winds originate from large volumes of air called air masses. The characteristics of an air mass depend on where it has spent the last few days or weeks.

- If it has been over the Equator (tropical) it is warm.
- If it has been over the Poles (polar) it is cold.
- If it has been over the sea (maritime) it is wet.
- If it has been over the land (continental) it is dry.

Air streams are movements of air from its source region. The UK lies at the intersection of five air masses, which gives us our changeable weather.

> **EXAM TIP**
>
> Remember to link your knowledge of these weather factors with the reasons behind the presence of different land uses in the case study areas you have already covered in this unit, such as the Cairngorms or the Yorkshire Dales.

Quick Test

1. Describe how you could identify from a weather map that the winds associated with a low pressure system or depression are stronger than those in a high pressure system or anticyclone.

2. List the four factors affecting weather in the UK.

3. On a sketch map of the UK, practice drawing and summarising the main characteristics of the air streams affecting it.

4. Why are places warmer at the Equator than at the Poles?

River landscapes

In this section of the course you will be expected to know about rivers and their valleys. You should be prepared to draw diagrams to help you explain how river features such as waterfalls and meanders are formed. You will also be expected to know and be able to identify the river stages shown on the reference maps below.

Diagram A
Upper Course Youthful Stage
Waterfalls, gorge, rapids,
interlocking spurs

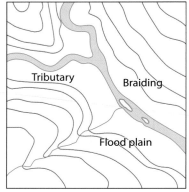

Diagram B
Middle Course Mature Stage
Meanders, river terraces, braiding
flood plain

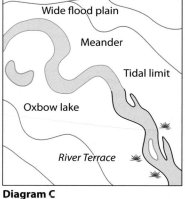

Diagram C
Lower Course Old Age Stage
Large meanders, oxbows,
deposition, marshland tidal waters

Fig 1.14 Landscapes on OS maps

The Ordnance Survey type maps (Fig 1.14) show the three typical river stages:

- Near the source in the mountains (Diagram A) the river is in the youthful stage.
- Lower downstream (Diagram B) is the mature stage in the middle of the river's course.
- At the end of the river's journey to the sea (Diagram C) the river goes into its old age stage.

Use the OS style maps and the table below to help you identify and understand the meaning of river features and how they occur on maps.

River stage	River course	River landscape	River features
A. Youthful	Upper course	Mountain stage	V-shaped valleys, waterfalls
B. Mature	Middle course	Valley stage	Meanders, braiding
C. Old age	Lower course	Plain stage	Oxbow lake, levee, flood plain

River processes

Rivers involve three processes: **erosion** of the landscape, **transportation** of sediment and **deposition** of sediment.

Erosion by rivers breaks the landscape down and in N5 Geography you should be able to explain how rivers erode their valleys using some of the following processes:

Hydraulic action

The river pushes air and water into cracks in the river bed and the rock breaks up.

Corrasion

Large and small fragments of rock such as pebbles and boulders rub the surface of the river bed, grinding it away.

Attrition

Rock fragments are carried by the river and collide and break up into smaller and smaller fragments.

Corrosion and solution

The river water dissolves the bedrock, for example acid rainwater will dissolve limestone.

Rivers **transport** the eroded materials along and may deposit them later (see meanders and levees on pages 19 and 20). Rivers move sediment in a number of ways. Large boulders are rolled along by the flow (**traction**), smaller rocks and boulders are bounced along the river bed (**saltation**), fine sediment floats in the flow of the river (**suspension**) and some material is dissolved and carried in the water itself (**solution**).

Quick Test

1. How do rivers erode the landscape?
2. What is hydraulic action?
3. What do the terms corrasion, attrition and solution mean?

The formation of river features

You should be able to recognise river landscape features on diagrams like those on page 20. You will also be expected to explain how some of these features were formed: most typically either a waterfall, a meander or an oxbow lake.

Formation of waterfalls

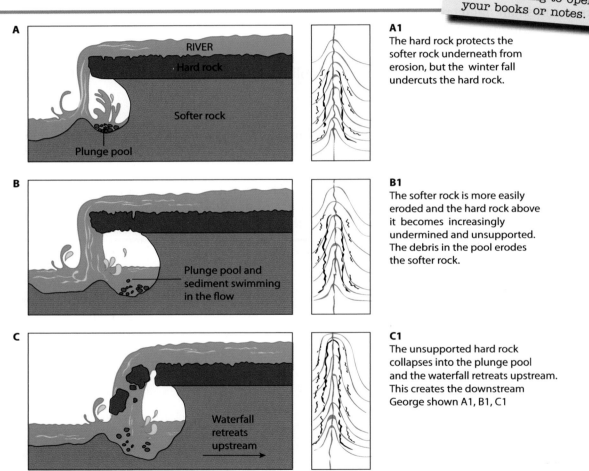

A1
The hard rock protects the softer rock underneath from erosion, but the winter fall undercuts the hard rock.

B1
The softer rock is more easily eroded and the hard rock above it becomes increasingly undermined and unsupported. The debris in the pool erodes the softer rock.

C1
The unsupported hard rock collapses into the plunge pool and the waterfall retreats upstream. This creates the downstream George shown A1, B1, C1

Fig 1.15 Formation of a waterfall and gorge

Waterfalls can be formed when a river flows over alternating beds of hard and soft rock (**A**). Erosion takes place using **hydraulic action**, where air and water is forced into the cracks in the bedrock, or **corrasion**, where the river grinds away at the bedrock using its load of sand and gravel. This erodes the weaker rock more than the harder rock above (**B**). Erosion undermines the hard rock on top until it cannot be supported and collapses into the stream (**C**). In this way, the river cuts backwards into the landscape, forming a waterfall and steep-sided gorge. The maps linked to each part of the diagram shows how the steep-sided rocky gorge gets longer and longer as the waterfall retreats.

How do meanders and ox bows form?

Rivers do not flow in a straight line. Contact between the river's water and the sides and bed make the water turbulent. Turbulent flow causes the water in the river to flow from side to side. This is called the river **meandering**. The speed of flow is greater in a meander on the outside of the bend so erosion takes place here (see Fig 1.16). Erosion takes place using **hydraulic action**, where air and water is forced into the cracks in the bedrock, or **corrasion**, where the river grinds away at the bedrock. On the inside of the bend, the flow rate is slower so the river deposits here. Over time, erosion of the outside bends into the neck of the **meander** sees the space in between eroded away more and more, until the river breaks through to form a new course. The old river course is abandoned and an **oxbow lake** is left behind.

EXAM TIP

Keywords for river landscape answers are: hydraulic action, abrasion, attrition, corrosion, undercutting, plunge pool, meander, oxbow lake and deposition.

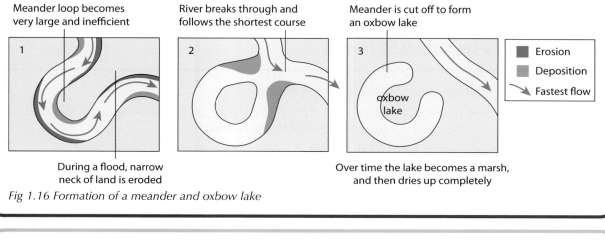

Meander loop becomes very large and inefficient

River breaks through and follows the shortest course

Meander is cut off to form an oxbow lake

Erosion
Deposition
Fastest flow

During a flood, narrow neck of land is eroded

Over time the lake becomes a marsh, and then dries up completely

Fig 1.16 Formation of a meander and oxbow lake

Other river processes

Use the erosion processes above to explain the formation of V-shaped river valleys. Braiding takes place where the river current is slow and sand and gravel is deposited by the river which causes the river to break up into several channels called braids. Use the transportation and erosion processes to explain this feature. Levees are found in the lower course where the river has created a low-lying flood plain. As the river bursts its banks its flow slows down as it leaves its channel. This leaves a deposit of sediment which over time builds up a raised bank alongside the river called a levee. Levees may prevent the river from flooding if people build them higher.

Quick Test

1. How does the river undermine the waterfall?
2. What is an oxbow lake?
3. How are levees formed?
4. **Exam-style question**: With the aid of an annotated diagram, explain how waterfalls are formed.
5. **Exam-style question**: Explain the formation of a meander. You may use diagrams to illustrate your answer.

Rivers on OS maps

You should be able to identify river features on an OS map and explain how they were formed. The diagrams below will help you spot the patterns associated with some of the main river features.

V-shaped river valley

Meander and oxbow lake

Levees to prevent flooding

Braided stream

Waterfall and gorge

Fig 1.17 Common river features

Exam-style questions

1. Study the Ordnance Survey map extract opposite.

    a) Describe the physical features of the river Allt Creag an Leith-choin from 972032 to where it enters Loch Morlich at 970093. **(4 marks)**

    b) Identify the features of glacial erosion found at each of the following grid references: 964026, 981028, 988035 and 004026. Choose from corrie and lochan; arête; hanging valley and U-shaped valley. **(3 marks)**

2. a) Using map evidence, describe and explain the advantages and environmental impact of tourism in the area as shown in the Cairngorms map extract. **(3 marks)**

    b) Explain how a corrie is formed. You may use diagram(s) to illustrate your answer. **(4 marks)**

3. Study the Ordnance Survey map extract opposite and the transect diagram below.

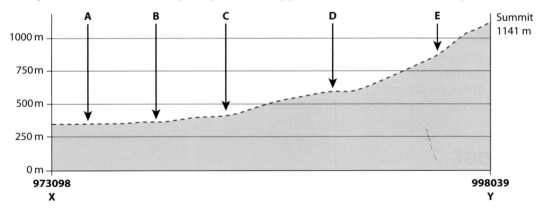

    a) Match the letters shown on the transect X-Y above to the following land features and land uses: ski area, river, forest edge, Fiacaill a' Coire Cais, forest track. **(3 marks)**

    b) To what extent do you agree that ski development may be at conflict with other land uses in the area of the map extract? **(4 marks)**

4. Answer the following question using map evidence.

   a) Describe the leisure and tourism features available on the map. **(3 marks)**

   b) Explain the benefits these leisure and tourism features bring to the area. **(4 marks)**

Fig 1.18 Cairngorms, scale 1:50 000

Fieldwork activities

A local river can be used to study river features in the real world, and this is a very effective way of learning about the way that rivers work in the landscape. There are a number of straightforward techniques that you can employ to study a river near you.

Investigating a burn or small stream

To prepare for your visit, follow these steps.

1. Identify the local study area on OS maps and on a satellite picture (for example, use Google Earth).

2. Search out a local geology map to see if geological features play a part in creating river features.

3. Access any information you can about the river on the Internet.

4. Create a sketch map to scale of the section or contrasting sections of the river under investigation.

5. Draw cross sections of the river at various points along its course, with lines showing the sections on the sketch map, and label the cross sections A–B, C–D etc.

6. Draw a long profile (long section) of the river.

On your field visit, use a digital camera to photograph river features such as waterfalls and meanders, and record the location of each feature on the sketch map. Remember to look at both features of erosion and deposition.

*   Draw annotated field sketches of points of interest you see on your visit to the burn. Include any man-made features, such as flood banks and weirs, to show how the river is being managed and to help judge how these features may change the way the river operates.

*   Use a flow meter to examine the flow across a meander at regular depths and create an Isovel diagram. Use the flow meter to measure flow velocity at various points of the river. Relate these measurements to things such as the stage the river is at, i.e. upper course or middle course etc. Relate these measurements to the cross sections and long profile you have drawn.

*   Measure the velocity of the surface flow over a set distance using a floating object such as an orange or tennis ball, by timing the object from point-to-point several times and taking an average velocity.

Writing up your results

One of the best ways to write up your results is to create a graphic display or an analysis sheet full of maps diagrams, photos and explanatory text. Here is an example.

Study of a local river – the Reekie Linn

The Reekie Linn is a waterfall and gorge on the River Isla in Angus, located where the river leaves the Grampian Highlands and enters the broad valley of Strathmore, near the small town of Alyth. Using the OS map of the area and Google Earth alongside a field visit, it is possible to complete a short study of the river and its spectacular features. In doing so, we can investigate why the waterfall formed here and what created the spectacular gorge.

Field study notes

Fig 1.19 Reekie Inn waterfall

Fig 1.20 Student sketch map of the Reekie Linn

Investigation of the Reekie Linn showed that the river flowed over hard volcanic rock (dolerite) at the point where it crossed the Highland Boundary Fault, which was underlain by softer old red sandstone rocks on the southern side of the fault.

Writing up

The field study notes can be used alongside your knowledge of how waterfalls form to explain how the Reekie Linn (or any other river feature near you) has formed. Measurements of small burns and rivers give you data that can be turned into useful graphs, for example to compare the speed of flow of the river at different stages in its course. Measurements could be taken across a meander to study the different depths and velocity of flow in the feature. Knowledge of local geology might help explain how rock type leads to waterfall formation in some cases. Rivers may be misfits if they have had glacial melt water flowing through them in the past and this could also form the basis of a study. The key thing is to be able to explain the river features you find.

Limestone scenery

In this section of the course you will be expected to know about **limestone scenery**, also called **karst scenery**. You should also be prepared to draw diagrams to help you explain how a range of limestone features are formed. You will also be expected to know and be able to identify on an OS map the range of limestone features detailed in this chapter.

Fig 1.21–1.23 Limestone structure

EXAM TIP
- Stalactite – **c** for ceiling, Stalagmite – **g** for ground.
- Stalactites hold on tight.

How does limestone form?

Limestone is a common rock found in many parts of the UK. It was created from the bodies of sea life in ancient seas. As the creatures died, they formed layers of limey ooze on the sea bed, creating layer after layer of rock beds separated by **horizontal bedding planes**. After the limestone formed it cracked vertically, caused by folding and earth movements and also the limestone shrinking as it dried out. These cracks are called **vertical joints**.

What makes limestone – and in particular carboniferous limestone – special, is the fact that it is soluble in rainwater and this produces a whole range of features found in limestone landscapes.

Diagrams like the one above can be drawn and labelled to help explain the formation of a number of limestone features from above and below ground. You will also have studied an area of limestone scenery, such as the Yorkshire Dales or the Peak District National Park, and this should provide examples of limestone features to add to your answer.

You need to be able to recognise a range of limestone features on a diagram. You should be able to spot these features on model landscape diagrams and as well as on OS maps. We will look at some of these features on page 26.

- **Above ground (surface)** – clints, grykes, limestone pavement, swallow hole, pot hole, sink hole, disappearing stream, gorge.
- **Below ground (subterranean)** – cavern, stalagmite, stalactite, pillar.

OS mapwork skills

You should be able to spot the following limestone features on OS maps like the one in this section and on the diagrams provided: limestone pavement, stalagmites and stalactites, limestone gorge, swallow holes and potholes, cave or cavern, clint, gryke, scree slopes, intermittent drainage.

Fig 1.24 Malham, scale 1:50 000

Exam-style question

Study the Yorkshire Dales National Park Ordnance Survey Map extract. Match the following grid references to the list of features of upland limestone

(i) Grid references: 876643, 893658, 900647, 914640
     Features: swallow hole, caves, gorge, limestone pavement

(ii) Select one of the features from the list above and explain how it was formed. You may use diagrams if you wish.

Quick Test

1. Why does rain water weather limestone?
2. How do clints, grykes and swallow holes form?
3. What would limestone pavement look like on an O.S. map?
4. How are stalactites and stalagmites created?

Limestone features: exam-style question

Question: How do limestone pavement and other limestone features form?

Limestone pavement

Limestone is made up of the shells and dead bodies of sea life. (1) It was laid down in beds. Each bed of limestone is separated from others by horizontal bedding planes. (1) As the limestone mass dried out, or as a consequence of earth movements, vertical cracks formed called joints. (1)

Falling rain dissolves carbon dioxide in the atmosphere, which turns it into weak carbonic acid. (1) This dissolves limestone, especially where the landscape was stripped bare of soil by glaciers that left the soluble rock open to attack. (1) Joints and bedding planes are especially under attack and are enlarged over time. (1)

The surface joints are dissolved to form crevices called grykes with upstanding blocks (clints) of limestone inbetween. (1) Large areas of clints and grykes can be found on the limestone uplands and are called limestone pavements because of their block structure. (1)

Other limestone features

Solution also creates other limestone features. Acid rain water forms streams that open up joints and bedding planes to form swallow holes (1) or water sinks (sink holes), where streams disappear underground, leaving dry valleys on the surface. (1) Joints and bedding planes can be opened up beneath the surface and eroded into massive caverns and connecting passages as water flows underground. (1) Underground streams eventually meet impermeable rock layers beneath the limestone, such as clay, and reappear on the surface as a resurgent stream. (1) These often resurface at the foot of a limestone scarp or scar (steep almost vertical rock face). (1)

Underground features

Stalagmites and stalactites are formed in caves and caverns from the water dripping from the ceiling of the cave. (1) This water is charged with calcium carbonate in solution. As the water drips from the ceiling of the cave, evaporation leaves behind a tiny deposit of calcium carbonate mineral called calcite. (1) This builds up like a stone icicle hanging from the roof of the cave and is called a **stalactite**. (1) The drips fall to the ground below, where calcite is deposited again to form a **stalagmite** (1), which grows upwards towards the roof. If a stalactite and stalagmite meet and join together, they form a pillar. (1)

EXAM TIPS

- Here are some keywords that will help with answers to limestone questions: joints, carbonic acid, permeable, impermeable, soluble, calcium carbonate, calcite.
- If the question says 'you may use a diagram(s)' then **think strongly about** using a diagram(s) to help your explanation. Diagrams score marks!
- Learn the landscape features you need in your answers by studying the diagrams provided here or in your notes. Practise drawing and labelling them.

Land use and land use conflict in limestone areas

Limestone hillsides with grass provide rough grazing for sheep and hill cattle

Forestry is rarely found on the alkaline limestone uplands

Impermeable Rock

Quarrying uses local rock like limestone mostly for building and construction

Gordale Scar Gorge

Scarp

Shake Holes

Swallow Hole

Limestone Pavement

Cavern
Stalactites
Stalagmites

Resurgent Stream

Scree

Impermeable Rock

Farming uses the valley floors where the clay soils are more fertile and allow the production of crops and better grazing

Tourists visit the National Park and are attracted by the scenery and opportunities for outdoor activities

Fig 1.25 Limestone features and land use

Gaping Gill Swallow Hole

Limestone Pavement

Malham Cove

Resurgent stream

Dry Valley

Gordale Scar Gorge

Waterfall

Limestone Pavement

Ingleborough

Fig 1.26 Limestone scenery

Limestone areas like the Yorkshire Dales are dominated by **sheep and hill cattle farming** because of the cool climate and poor soils found on the limestone hills. Crops can only be grown in the sheltered valley bottoms on more fertile clay soils. Farms tend to be large and employ a lot of rough grazing.

Limestone is used widely in the construction industry for building stone and for cement making. It is also used by the chemical industry, so **quarrying** is an important economic activity in areas like the Yorkshire Dales and the Peak District National Parks.

EXAM TIP

Use the diagram from this section to help you to visualise the limestone landscape being talked about.

What land use conflicts occur in limestone areas?

Farming and tourism

Conflicts can break out between farmers and tourists in the National Parks, especially if visitors do not follow relevant parts of the Countryside Code (www.naturalengland.org.uk):

- Leave gates and property as you find them and follow paths unless wider access is available.
- Keep dogs under effective control.
- Leave no trace of your visit and take your litter home.

Tourists and walkers may cause problems if they allow livestock to escape or if dogs are allowed to run loose among livestock, especially where there are lambs or calves. Livestock let loose onto roads is a traffic hazard and can be injured by passing cars.

Conflict with farmers can be resolved in various ways:

Fig 1.27 Dogs should be kept under close control

- Providing information to visitors about behaving responsibly in the countryside. The country code lays out rights and responsibilities, and citizenship education in schools underpins this.
- Farmers help manage visitor pressures by providing good access routes with gates and stiles, and provide notices and signs that guide walkers and visitors using their land.
- Dogs are kept on leads or under close control.
- Fences and walls are well maintained and footpaths are built where erosion has been caused by too many people using a particular route.

Limestone quarrying

Limestone for cement and building material is an important economic resource and quarrying and cement production employs many thousands of people in Britain. It therefore makes a significant contribution to the economy. It is an activity that has gone on for generations, even in the National Parks.

Quarrying does have environmental effects and can come into conflict with the needs of those who wish to conduct tourist activities. People object to quarrying and cement production for a variety of reasons:

- Excavation and processing limestone creates ugly scars in the landscape, spoiling local views.
- Blasting operations cause disturbance and can close off nearby areas.
- Large amounts of dust are generated and this can affect the landscape nearby.
- Narrow country roads are affected by heavy lorries carrying rock and cement, causing congestion and traffic hold-ups at busy times.
- Wildlife may be disturbed.

Against this, the quarry companies point out that the industry plays an important part in the economy and was always present in the National Park areas. They also employ many local people in areas that have few other jobs.

Conflict with the quarrying industry is resolved by agreements that manage the impact of excavation of limestone and its manufacture into cement.

- Screens of trees help mask or reduce the visual impact of quarries.
- Blasting may be restricted to times that cause the least disturbance to tourism and to local residents.
- HGV movement on the roads is scheduled to avoid busy times.
- Quarries are damped down with water to reduce dust and HGV trailers are covered to reduce dust dispersal.
- Railways and special wagons are used instead of road transport.
- Old quarry workings are restored to good condition or are converted to nature friendly sites by planting woodland, or establishing ponds and wetlands suitable for water birds and other wildlife.
- Derelict buildings are removed.
- Rock faces can be used for climbing, helping the local economy once quarrying has stopped.

Quick Test

1. Why might quarrying disturb wildlife?
2. How might quarrying affect tourist income?
3. How effective are measures taken to control the impact of quarrying?
4. **Exam-style question:** For an area you have studied, describe one example of land use conflict and explain how it was resolved. Use the information on Fig 1.25 to help you.

Glaciation

The starting point of a glacier is a hollow high on the mountainside, a corrie. Snow accumulates above the snowline. Below the snowline is the ablation zone where the snow melts in summer and the glacier begins to retreat.

Fig 1.28 Mer de Glace Glacier, France

Key processes

- **Erosion**– As a glacier moves downhill it wears away the land it moves over. (See plucking and abrasion below.)
- **Transportation**– The movement of material by the glacier. Referred to as load or moraine.
- **Deposition** – At the snout (the end of the glacier), the ice melts and its load is dumped or deposited.

EXAM TIP

Use the key processes when explaining landform formations.

Processes of erosion

Ice is a powerful agent of erosion in two ways:

1. **Plucking** – ice freezes onto rock and when the ice moves it pulls a piece of rock away: the tweezer effect.

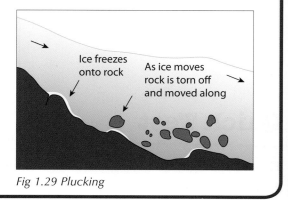

Ice freezes onto rock

As ice moves rock is torn off and moved along

Fig 1.29 Plucking

2. **Abrasion** – pieces of rock carried by the ice scrape at the surrounding rock and erode it away: the sandpaper effect.

Fig 1.30 Abrasion

Freeze-thaw weathering is also wearing away the landscape. Water in small cracks in rock will freeze, expand and widen the cracks. Repeated freezing and thawing will cause rocks to shatter. A scree slope can form.

Fig 1.31 Freeze-thaw weathering

Named glaciated uplands

Some of the UK's glaciated uplands are now designated as National Parks. Make sure you can locate upland glaciated areas on a map of the British Isles.

Key:

1: Cairngorm

2: Loch Lomond and The Trossachs

4: The Lake District

14: Snowdonia

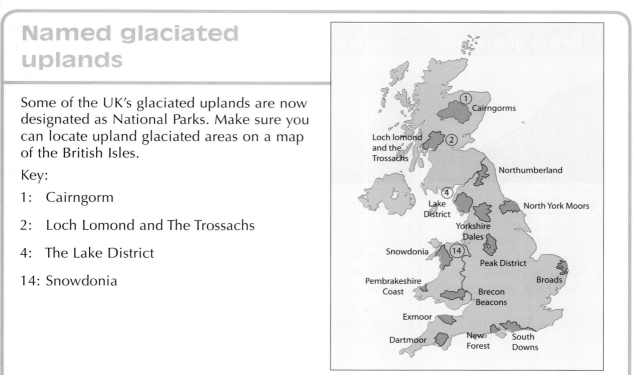

Fig 1.32 Map of UK National Parks

Quick Test

1. What are the key processes of glacial erosion?
2. What work does a glacier do?

Landforms of erosion

Formation of a corrie

A corrie is an armchair-shaped hollow, and examples of this can be seen at Coire an t-Sneacdha or Coire Cas.

Fig 1.33 A corrie

Before glaciation	During glaciation	After glaciation

Fig 1.34 Formation of a corrie

• Snow accumulates in a hollow (usually north-facing). • Snow is compressed into neve, then glacial ice. • Freeze-thaw action takes place at the top of the hill where rock is exposed.	• The glacier moves downhill because of gravity, in a rotational manner. • Plucking steepens the back wall. • Abrasion deepens the hollow.	• The ice melts, leaving a hollow in the mountain side. • A rock lip may form, caused by rotation. • Melt water may be trapped by moraine and form a corrie lochan or tarn. • A scree slope may form.

When two or more corries are found back-to-back and a steep knife-edge ridge is formed it is called an **arête**, such as Helvellyn in the Lake District. When three or more corries form back-to-back a frost-shattered, horned peak called a **pyramidal peak** can occur, for example the Matterhorn in Switzerland.

Three-stage formation of a U-shaped valley

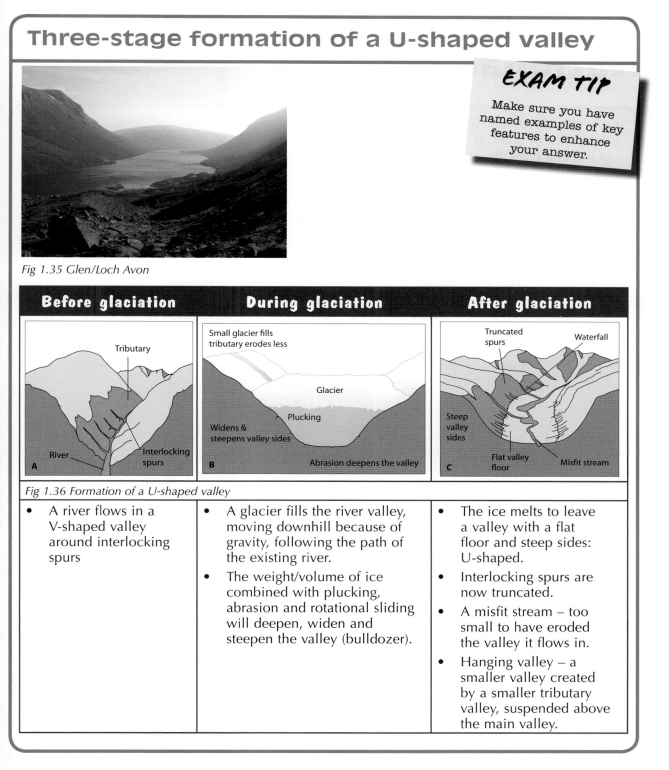

Fig 1.35 Glen/Loch Avon

EXAM TIP

Make sure you have named examples of key features to enhance your answer.

Fig 1.36 Formation of a U-shaped valley

Before glaciation	During glaciation	After glaciation
• A river flows in a V-shaped valley around interlocking spurs	• A glacier fills the river valley, moving downhill because of gravity, following the path of the existing river. • The weight/volume of ice combined with plucking, abrasion and rotational sliding will deepen, widen and steepen the valley (bulldozer).	• The ice melts to leave a valley with a flat floor and steep sides: U-shaped. • Interlocking spurs are now truncated. • A misfit stream – too small to have eroded the valley it flows in. • Hanging valley – a smaller valley created by a smaller tributary valley, suspended above the main valley.

Quick Test

1. What are the main processes of erosion and how do they work?

2. Name some of the main glacial landscape features in an area you have studied.

Case study – Cairngorm National Park

Cairngorm National Park, home to Britain's highest and largest mountain range, was established in 2003. It covers an area of 4,528km². It is a good example of a glaciated upland that provides a wealth of land uses. It is managed and protected by a number of organisations including the National Park Authority. See http://cairngorms.co.uk/look-after for further information.

Corrie
Horshoe-shaped contours

Arête
Cliff-like ridge between two corries

Misfit stream

U-shaped valley
Steep sides (contours close together) and flat floor. Often filled with water to make a ribbon lake

Fig 1.37 Glacial features

Land uses

Tourism: in summer, or more importantly during the main winter ski season, Cairngorm is visited by up to 5000 tourists a day. Visitors use the funicular railway to access the mountain for skiing, or to visit the Ptarmigan Restaurant. The area is popular for walking and mountain biking or sightseeing (passive tourism).

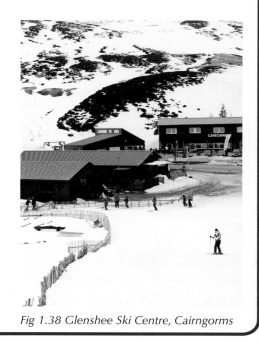

Fig 1.38 Glenshee Ski Centre, Cairngorms

Conservation: the National Park is protected by law but many conservation groups take an interest in preserving the natural landscape and managing its use.

Farming: the steep valley sides and thin soils are ideal for sheep grazing or keeping deer to be sold for venison. In the flat valley floors, some crops can be grown, such as barley, or hay for animal feed.

Quarrying: granite is quarried for building purposes, making good use of the natural stone.

Forestry: plantation forestry is ideal for growing in the sub-arctic climate. The Caledonian Scots Pine is being re-introduced as a native species.

Fig 1.39 Deer, Cairngorms National Park

EXAM TIP

Land users can be in conflict with each other – you must know the conflict and solutions to the conflict, for a named case study area.

Quick Test

1. Explain how a corrie is formed.
2. What conflicts might arise in a National Park between tourists and other users?
3. How can National Parks be managed?

The coast – erosion

The coast is the boundary between the land and sea.

The coastal system

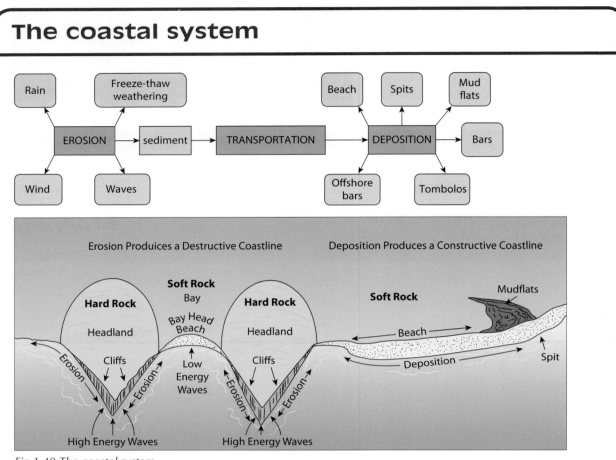

Fig 1.40 The coastal system

Key processes

There are three key coastal processes:

- **Erosion** – as the waves move, they wear away the coastline. See hydraulic action, attrition, corrosion and corrasion below.
- **Transportation** – the movement of material by the wave. See constructive and destructive waves and longshore drift on page 40.
- **Deposition** – when the waves run out of energy, material is dumped.

Erosion: what factors determine the shape of the coast?

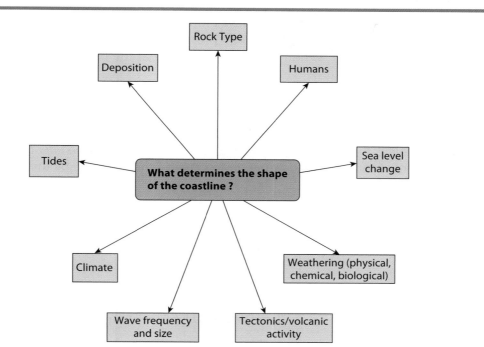

Waves

Waves are the most effective agent of erosion along the coastline. They are created by the wind blowing over the surface of the sea. Their size is determined by:

- the fetch – the distance over which the wave travels
- the wind speed
- the depth of the water – this controls wave height

Fig 1.41 Constructive and destructive waves

Coastal landforms resulting from erosion

The sea erodes in four ways:

- **Hydraulic action** – the power of the waves hitting the cliffs causes water and air to be forced into the cracks in the rocks at high pressure. This causes the cracks to widen, splitting a section of cliff. When the waves cut away at the base of a cliff, the process is called undercutting.
- **Attrition** – The materials being carried by the sea are being constantly worn down by knocking into each other, making them into smaller, rounder particles.
- **Corrosion** – Softer rock such as chalk or limestone is gradually dissolved by sea water.
- **Corrasion** – This is the wearing away of the coastline by the erosive effect of sand, shingle and boulders, i.e. a load being hurled against the coastline by the waves.

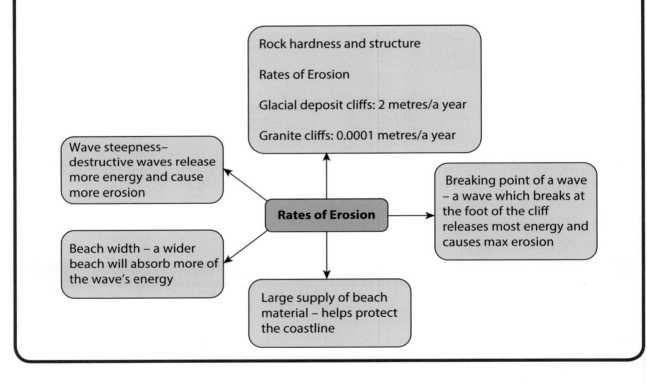

Rock hardness and structure

Rates of Erosion

Glacial deposit cliffs: 2 metres/a year

Granite cliffs: 0.0001 metres/a year

Wave steepness– destructive waves release more energy and cause more erosion

Beach width – a wider beach will absorb more of the wave's energy

Rates of Erosion

Breaking point of a wave – a wave which breaks at the foot of the cliff releases most energy and causes max erosion

Large supply of beach material – helps protect the coastline

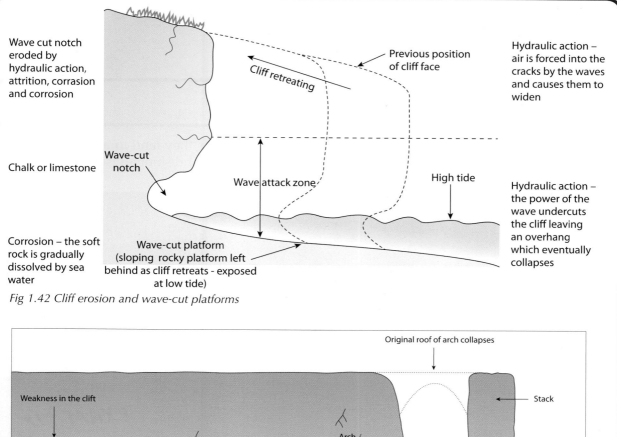

Wave cut notch eroded by hydraulic action, attrition, corrasion and corrosion

Chalk or limestone

Corrosion – the soft rock is gradually dissolved by sea water

Wave-cut notch

Cliff retreating

Previous position of cliff face

Wave attack zone

Wave-cut platform (sloping rocky platform left behind as cliff retreats - exposed at low tide)

High tide

Hydraulic action – air is forced into the cracks by the waves and causes them to widen

Hydraulic action – the power of the wave undercuts the cliff leaving an overhang which eventually collapses

Fig 1.42 Cliff erosion and wave-cut platforms

Original roof of arch collapses

Weakness in the clift

Cave

Arch

Stack

Stump

The sea attacks the foot of the cliff and erodes an area of weakness

Crack gets larger and develops into a small cave

Cave is widened and deepend until it cuts through the headland to form a gap

Further undercutting causes the arch to collapse. This leaves part of the cliff detached as a stack. Further undercutting causes the stack to collapse

Fig 1.43 Coastal landforms

Quick Test

1. What 3 factors determine the size of a wave?
2. Identify two differences between a constructive wave and a destructive wave.
3. What happens in the process of undercutting?

The coast – transportation and deposition

Transportation

Remember, waves rarely approach the coast at right angles. As they tend to approach it at an angle determined by the wind direction, eroded material (sand/shingle) is moved in a zigzag course along the coast.

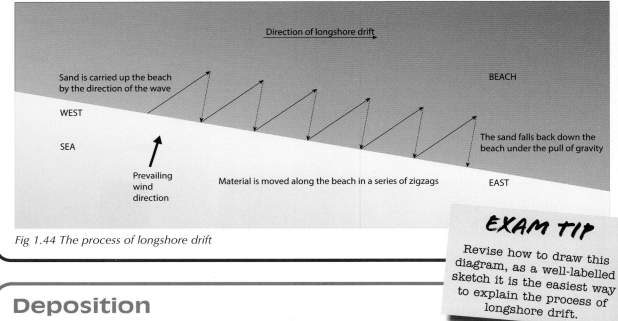

Fig 1.44 The process of longshore drift

EXAM TIP

Revise how to draw this diagram, as a well-labelled sketch it is the easiest way to explain the process of longshore drift.

Deposition

Coastal landforms resulting from deposition:

- **Beaches** – these are the result of deposition of eroded material usually between headlands.
- **Spits**

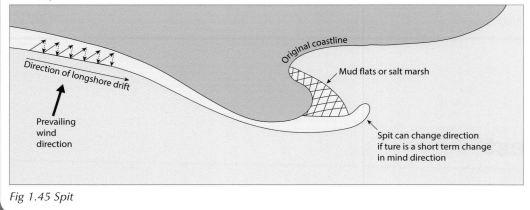

Fig 1.45 Spit

- These are long, narrow ridges of sand or shingle.
- They occur where the coastline changes direction.
- They extend into the sea or part-way across a river estuary.
- Sand spits are formed by constructive waves.
- Shingle spits are formed by destructive waves.
- Many spits develop a hooked or curved end due to a change in the prevailing wind direction.
- Examples of spits: Spurn Head, the Holderness coast.

- **Bars** – if a spit extends across a bay that links two headlands, or across a river estuary, it is called a bar. An example of a bar is Slapton Sands, South Devon.

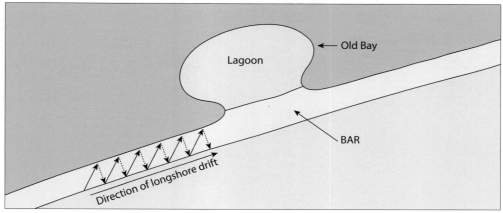

Fig 1.46 Bar

- **Barrier beach** – this is where a spit extends across a shallow bay. An example of a barrier beach is Slapton Sands, south Devon.
- **Tombolo** – this occurs when a sand spit grows outwards into open water and reaches an island. An example of a tombolos is Chesil Beach in Dorset (this joins the Dorset coast with the Isle of Portland).
- **Sand dunes** – dry sand is picked up off the beach by the wind and then it gets trapped by seaweed or driftwood. It gradually piles up until it is colonized by vegetation and in time grows in size to form dunes. An example of a sand dune is Gullane, East Lothian.

Quick Test

1. What is meant by the 'fetch' of a wave?
2. How do constructive and destructive waves differ?
3. List four ways in which the sea erodes and name three examples of landforms resulting from coastal erosion.
4. Describe the process of longshore drift.

Coastal land uses

Very little of the coastline of the UK is 'unused' – the vast majority of our approximately 5,000-mile coast has a wide variety of land uses (or activities) and habitats, both human and natural.

You will have studied particular case studies but you will soon find that there are land uses and conflicts/themes that are common features of many coastal areas. Take the famous Dorset coastline in southern England:

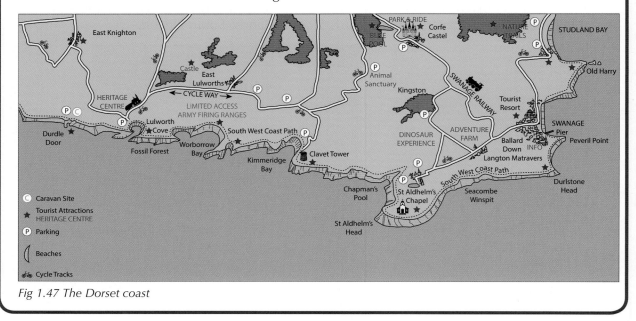

Fig 1.47 The Dorset coast

Pressures on the coastline

- **Retreating or crumbling cliffs** – caused by increased erosion, quarrying, caravan sites, extreme weather.
- **Pollution** – rubbish dumped or washed up on beaches: particularly plastics, sewage. UK beaches are under pressure to meet EU standards of cleanliness (Blue Flag beaches).

Fig 1.48 Waste on a Scottish beach

- **Industrial development** – natural harbours and their surrounding flat hinterlands attract shipping and industry, for example Milford Haven, which is a deep water port, South Wales, and Grangemouth oil refinery, West Lothian.

- **Military uses** – these have restricted local and tourist access due to live firing, for example Tyneham and Worbarrow Bay, South Dorset, and the Kirkcudbright coast, South West Scotland.

- **Increased tourism** – disadvantages: increase traffic, pollution, noise, litter, increased house prices, second homes; advantages: jobs, increased local income.

- **Reduced supply of sediment to beaches, dune systems, spits and bars** – this is caused by hard engineering further up the coast, for example harbours, sea walls, groynes, marinas, jetties and piers may interrupt longshore drift.

- **Global warming** – When sea levels rise there is a greater incidence of extreme weather events such as storms and hurricanes.

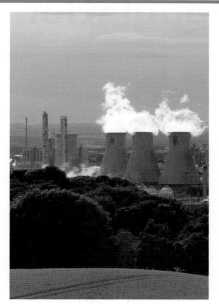

Fig 1.49 Grangemouth oil refinery

Fig 1.50 Crowded beach, Weston-Super-Mare

Quick Test

1. Study the map and identify all the land uses along this stretch of coast.
2. What pressures might there be on this coastline?

Population distribution

Population distribution is all about **where people live and why**.

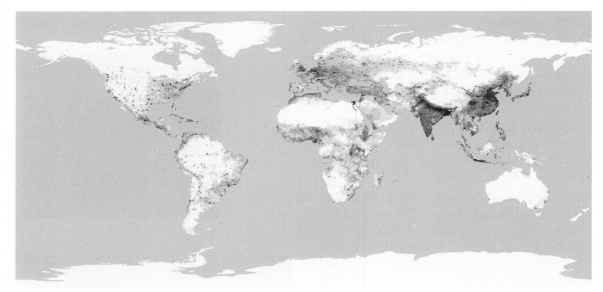

Fig 2.1 Worldwide population distribution

Population is unevenly distributed around the world. Some places are crowded and have a high population density and other areas are empty and have a low population density.

Population density is a measurement of people per square kilometre. It is calculated by the formula: Area(sq km) ÷ Total Population.

Below there is information about a selection of countries of varying population densities including some of the positive and negative reasons why people choose to live in one area of the world and not in another.

UK

Land area: 244,820 km^2

Total population: 63,395,574

Average population density (people per km^2): 247

Positive characteristics:	Negative characteristics:	Main influencing factors determining population density:
• Moderate climate (i.e. reliable precipitation and sunshine) • Areas of flat, fertile land either in river valleys or lowland plains • Natural resources (e.g. fossil fuels – coal, gas and oil) • Coastal plains suitable for industry and trade	• Areas of high ground with steep slopes and poor soils • Higher than average precipitation and low temperatures, e.g. Scottish Highlands, Snowdonia and Lake District	• Climate • Availability of flat land • Fertile soils • Availability of natural resources • Accessibility (good road and rail links and ports)

Kenya

Land area: 582,650 km²

Total population: 44,037,656

Average population density
(people per km²): 58

Positive characteristics:	Negative characteristics:	Main influencing factors determining population density:
• Fertile highlands • Flat coastal plain	• Tropical (along the coast) to arid climate with the risk of drought • Scarcity of surface water resources • Lack of natural resources • Disease, e.g. malaria, biharzia, schistosomiasis • Little government investment	• Climate • Water scarcity • Lack of natural resources • Mosquitoes and other disease spreading insects

Bangladesh

Land area: 144,000 km²

Total population: 163,654,860

Average population density
(people per km²): 1,002

Positive characteristics:	Negative characteristics:	Main influencing factors determining population density:
• Monsoon climate with reliable precipitation • Plenty of flat land • Fertile river valleys and coastal plains	• Lack of natural resources • High risk of flooding	• Fertile soils • Flat land

Germany

Land area: 357,021 km²

Total population: 81,147,265

Average population density
(people per km²): 231

Positive characteristics:	Negative characteristics:	Main influencing factors determining population density:
• Moderate climate • Fertile and sheltered river valleys, e.g. the Rhine • Plenty of flat land • Good accessibility • Plenty of natural resources, e.g. coal, iron ore in the Ruhr valley	• None	• Climate • Natural resources • Flat land • Accessibility • At the heart of Europe • Large Government investment

Unit 2: Human Environments

The table on the previous page should help you see why people choose one area of the world to live over another area. Key sustainability concepts to consider include:

EXAM TIP

Make sure you can identify a list of reasons for why some places are empty and others are crowded.

- **Optimum population** – where the amount of resources can support the population.
- **Underpopulation** – where there are too few people to utilise the resources available.
- **Overpopulation** – where there are not enough resources to support the population.

The following photographs and accompanying table show how we might assess the positive and negative characteristics of various parts of the world and assess their suitability to sustain a population.

Photo	General description	Positive or negative area	What are the factors?
Fig 2.2 Great Basin Desert, Utah, USA	Arid desert	Negative	• Lack of precipitation • Water scarcity • No soil, bare earth
Fig 2.3 New York, USA	Large natural harbour	Positive	• Sheltered harbour • Flat land either side of the Hudson River • Access to the Atlantic Ocean and Europe

	High mountains	Negative	• Very steep slopes • Thin soils • Cold winters • Poor accessibility
Fig 2.4 Himalayas, Nepal			
	Flat, fertile lowlands	Positive	• Flat land • Fertile soils • Moderate precipitation
Fig 2.5 Sri Lanka			

Quick Test

1. Identify 3 positive characteristics which have encouraged a higher population density.
2. Identify 3 negative characteristics which have lead to a lower population density.
3. Give an example of an area with a higher population density and explain why it has such a high density.
4. Give an example of an area with a low population density and explain why it has such a low density.

World population growth

The world's population has now reached over 7 billion. If you look at the world population graph below you will see that there has been a population explosion (where population grows very rapidly) since 1930. This explosion has largely been the result of a rapid rise of the number of people living in the developing world.

Why does the population change?

The rate at which the world's population increases or decreases depends on the 'balance' between birth rates, death rates and migration.

- **Birth rate** – the number of live births per 1000 people per year.
- **Death rate** – the number of deaths per 1000 people per year.
- **Migration** – the number of people moving in or out of an area.

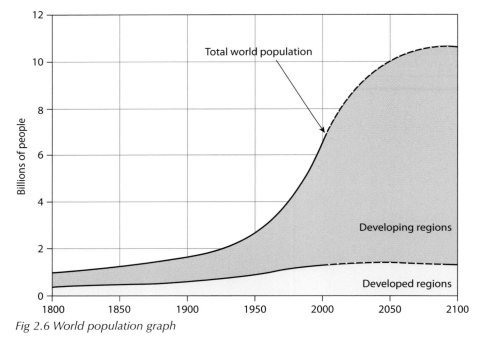

Fig 2.6 World population graph

The difference between the birth rate and the death rate is called natural increase. With a **natural increase**, the birth rate is higher. With a **natural decrease,** the death rate is higher. Since the beginning of the 20th century there has been a high natural increase as the birth rate has exceeded the death rate.

Life expectancy

Life expectancy is the average number of years a person is expected to live. This indicates a good health care system and a well-balanced diet in a country, i.e. Japan's life expectancy is 84 years but South Africa's is only 49 years.

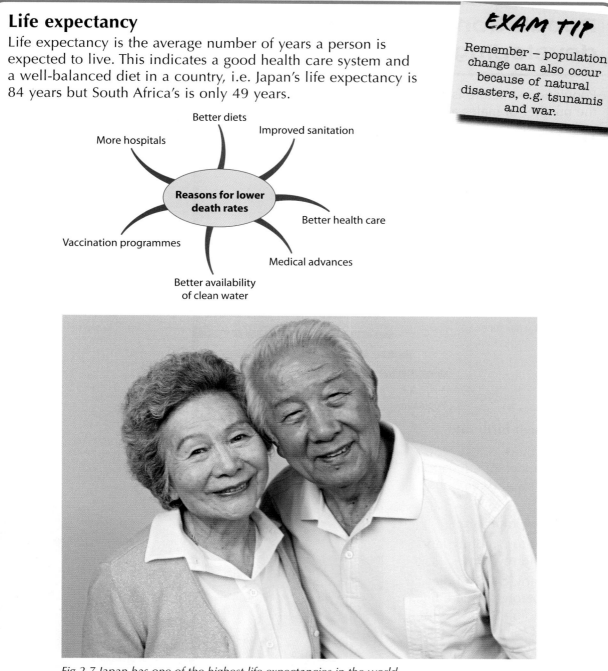

More hospitals · Better diets · Improved sanitation

Reasons for lower death rates

Vaccination programmes · Better availability of clean water · Medical advances · Better health care

Fig 2.7 Japan has one of the highest life expectancies in the world

Quick Test

1. Write down the definitions of birth rate, death rate and natural increase.
2. What other variable can cause population change in an area?
3. Give three reasons for death rates falling worldwide.
4. Give two reasons why developing countries have high birth rates and two reasons why in some developed countries (i.e. Hungary and Germany) the birth rate has recently fallen below the death rate.

Population structures in developed and developing countries

Population structure is shown by a type of graph called a population pyramid. It shows the number of males and females in different age groups.

Developing country – Kenya

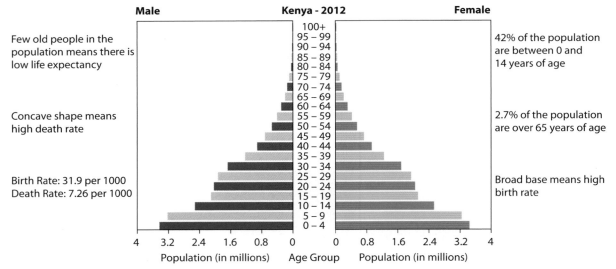

Few old people in the population means there is low life expectancy

Concave shape means high death rate

Birth Rate: 31.9 per 1000
Death Rate: 7.26 per 1000

42% of the population are between 0 and 14 years of age

2.7% of the population are over 65 years of age

Broad base means high birth rate

Kenya's high birth rate

In Kenya there is less birth control, a lack of education and cultural and religious pressures.

Some viewpoints are:

– 'I want to hand my land down to my sons.'

– 'So many children die here before they are five, I am going to have a lot so that I am sure at least some will survive.'

– 'I need my children to help in the fields and make me important in my village.'

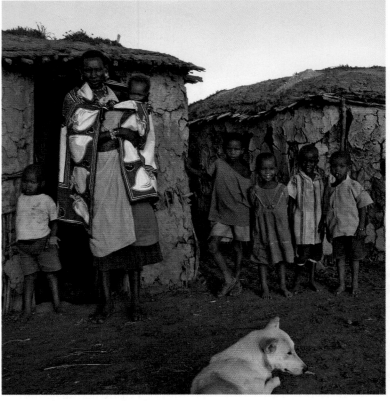

Fig 2.8 A large Kenyan family

Developed country – United Kingdom

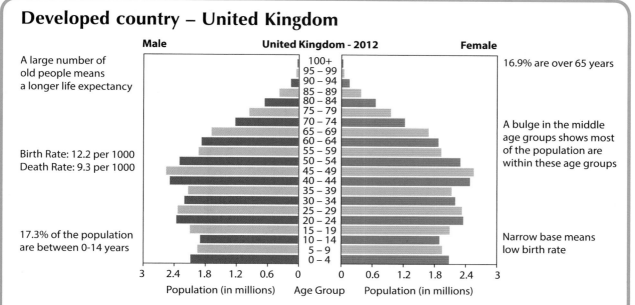

Male   **United Kingdom - 2012**   **Female**

A large number of old people means a longer life expectancy

16.9% are over 65 years

Birth Rate: 12.2 per 1000
Death Rate: 9.3 per 1000

A bulge in the middle age groups shows most of the population are within these age groups

17.3% of the population are between 0-14 years

Narrow base means low birth rate

Age groups: 100+, 95 – 99, 90 – 94, 85 – 89, 80 – 84, 75 – 79, 70 – 74, 65 – 69, 60 – 64, 55 – 59, 50 – 54, 45 – 49, 40 – 44, 35 – 39, 30 – 34, 25 – 29, 20 – 24, 15 – 19, 10 – 14, 5 – 9, 0 – 4

Scale (Male, left): 3, 2.4, 1.8, 1.2, 0.6, 0
Scale (Female, right): 0, 0.6, 1.2, 1.8, 2.4, 3
Population (in millions)   Age Group   Population (in millions)

The UK's low birth rate

In the UK, contraception is readily available. More women work compared to women in Kenya, and family planning is countrywide.

Some viewpoints are:

- 'Children cannot work until they are 16 so it will cost me a great deal to have a large family.'
- 'Contraception is freely available and it is very rare for a child to die.'

Fig 2.9 A British family

Quick Test

1. What is the graph called that shows population structure?
2. If the population pyramid has a broad base what does this indicate about the population structure?
3. If the population pyramid is concave what does this indicate about the population structure?

How does the population change over time?

The Demographic Transition Model is a multiple line graph that shows how population changes over time.

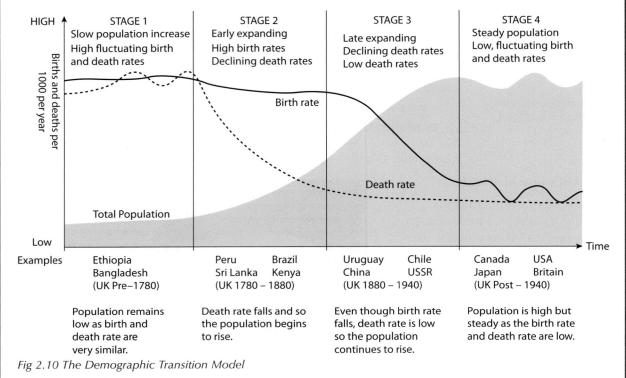

	STAGE 1	STAGE 2	STAGE 3	STAGE 4
	Slow population increase High fluctuating birth and death rates	Early expanding High birth rates Declining death rates	Late expanding Declining death rates Low death rates	Steady population Low, fluctuating birth and death rates
Examples	Ethiopia Bangladesh (UK Pre–1780)	Peru Brazil Sri Lanka Kenya (UK 1780 – 1880)	Uruguay Chile China USSR (UK 1880 – 1940)	Canada USA Japan Britain (UK Post – 1940)
	Population remains low as birth and death rate are very similar.	Death rate falls and so the population begins to rise.	Even though birth rate falls, death rate is low so the population continues to rise.	Population is high but steady as the birth rate and death rate are low.

Fig 2.10 The Demographic Transition Model

Sometimes Stage 5 is added to this model to show population decline in some developed countries (e.g. Switzerland and Hungary) caused by birth rates dropping below death rates.

What problems are created by a changing population?

Within any population there is a **dependant (ageing and youthful)** population – these are the people of non-working age, either 0–15 years or over 65 years. They are dependent on the **economically active** population – those people between 16 and 64 years of age.

Developed countries	Developing countries
High number of elderly (**ageing**) dependants because of increased life expectancy.	High number of young (youthful) dependants, because of high birth rates.
Problems caused by this trend: • Older people require more spending on health care • Greater need for public services, e.g. social services, hospitals • Increased number of care/retirement homes required • Increased taxation of the economically active population to fund these requirements • Increased strain on a country's finances • Fewer young people means there will be less of an economically active population in the future	Problems caused by this trend: • Overcrowding • Poverty • Unemployment • Education and health care services are not able to meet needs • Inadequate housing – informal settlement and/or shanty towns spring up • Lack of formal employment leads to the growth of informal sector jobs, e.g. hawking • Increased crime rates • Lack of infrastructure and basic facilities, e.g. clean water, waste disposal

Quick Test

1.   What are the four stages of the Demographic Transition model?

Urban land use zones

What do we mean by the term urban?

The term **urban** refers to large towns, cities and conurbations. A **conurbation** is a large, **continuous built-up area** created by towns and cities expanding and growing together.

Characteristics of land use zones in the developed world

The term **land use zone** refers to the way that people use areas of a city or town. Often it is useful to think of these in diagrammatical form and to look at a **transect** from the centre of a city to the edge like the one opposite. A transect defines a series of zones that transition from sparse rural farmhouses to the dense urban core.

Urban land use models

In large towns and cities, it is often possible to see a clear pattern of land use which reflects the development of the settlement. The distribution of urban land use can be explained using **models of urban land use** such as those shown below. In Fig 2.12, the concentric rings model is evident.

■ Central business district (CBD)	Modern housing
■ 19th century housing and industry	Modern industrial estate
Older high class housing	

Concentric rings model where the city has grown outwards from its old centre.

Sector model where the city has grown around transport lines such as canals or railway lines.

Multiple nuclei model where the city has grown around more than one centre (or CBD).

Local business district

Commercial district

Fig 2.11 Urban land use models

Note the contrast between developed world cities and developing world cities (see pages 57–61).

Rural-urban fringe	Suburbs	Inner city	Central business district (C.B.D.)	Inner city	Suburbs	Rural-urban fringe
• New industry • One/two storey buildings • Main roads (e.g. motorways) • Green belt • Commuter villages	• Modern late 20th or early 21st century semi-detached and detached housing • Gardens and greenery • Low density • High quality environment	• Transition zone • First developed in the 19th century • Grid iron street pattern • Large factories (often derelict) • High density of tenement or terraced housing • Lack of greenery and open space	• Department shops • Large offices • Main railway and bus stations • Many churches, pubs, clubs and cinemas and the town hall • Easily accessible - the main roads head into the C.B.D. • Highest land value • High building density • Tall buildings • Traffic congestion • The oldest part of the city • Grid iron or medieval street pattern • Subject to constant change	• High rise flats • Derelict land and waste ground • Derelict land, vandalism, crime, poverty, unemployment and other social and economic problems – related to industrial decline • Redevelopment occurring • Environmental improvements exist in some areas • Mixture of old and newer buildings • New houses of mixed type • Recent regeneration to encourage more people to live there	• Well-planned • Street patterns of crescents and cul-de-sacs • Some outer-city council estates with flats, high rise and mixed housing • Growth of car ownership, commuting and demand for quieter and safer residential environments have led to the growth of these areas • Houses with garages	• Room for expansion • Industrial estates • New housing estates

Fig 2.12 A city in the concentric land use model

Look at how buildings change in different zones of land use models.

Fig 2.13 Sydney CBD

Fig 2.14 Bangkok inner city

Fig 2.15 Suburbs of Arizona

Quick Test

1. What is a conurbation?

2. Describe the different kind of buildings you might find in the suburbs, the inner city and the C.B.D.

Recent developments or changes in a developing world city

The rapid growth of cities in developing countries – rural to urban migration

You must also learn a specific case study related to a developing world city and be able to apply it to questions in the SQA exam. Cities in the developing world have grown rapidly in the past 25–30 years.

The movement of people from the countryside (rural) to towns and cities is called rural-urban migration. This movement is due to rural push factors and urban pull factors. Often the pull factors are greater than the push factors. Rural families perceive that the city offers greater opportunities than the countryside, but the reality is often very different. Migrants arrive without money and are often homeless, living in temporary shelters made of waste materials.

Urban pull
Better job opportunities
Higher potential earnings
Better health and education services
Better amenities and infrastructure

Rural push
Poor job opportunities, low pay
Poor health and education services
Less access to service and industrial jobs

Fig 2.16 Urban pull and rural push

Urban land use within cities in developing countries

As in cities in the developed world, cities in developing countries acquire recognisable patterns of land use over time. These differ from the patterns in developed countries in a number of ways:

- High quality housing is located nearest to the C.B.D. (1)
- The quality of housing decreases rapidly towards the edge of town where slums or shanty towns develop (4)
- Industry is located along main roads leading into the city centre (6)

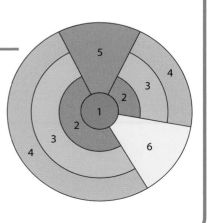

Case study – Rio de Janeiro

Rio de Janeiro is the second largest city in Brazil. It is an important centre of business and industry but is also a city of contrasts with old and new buildings, motorways and dirt tracks, and shacks and skyscrapers sitting side-by-side.

Rio is divided into five zones – Centro, North Zone, South Zone, West Zone and Barra da Tijuca. The photograph here shows the statue of Christ. His left arm is pointing towards the North Zone and his right arm to the South Zone.

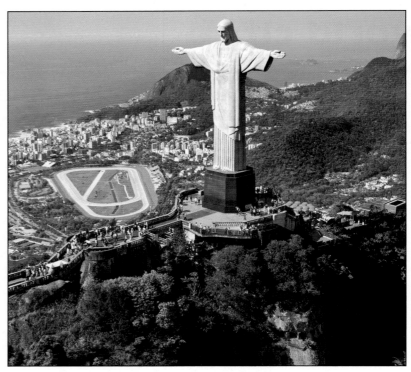

Fig 2.17 Christ the Redeemer, Rio de Janerio, Brazil

Problems in developing cities – Rio

In most cities within developing countries there are extreme contrasts between housing for the rich and housing for the poor who are forced to live in shanty towns (favelas) on the edge of the city, such as Rocinha, shown here.

Fig 2.18 Rocinha: a shanty town (favela) in Rio

Problems in Rio

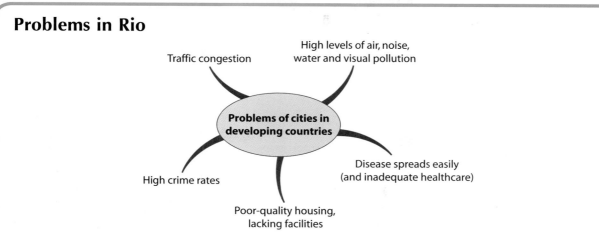

- Traffic congestion
- High levels of air, noise, water and visual pollution

Problems of cities in developing countries

- Disease spreads easily (and inadequate healthcare)
- High crime rates
- Poor-quality housing, lacking facilities

Solutions to problems in Rio

One-third of the people living in Rio live in squatter settlements. Local authorities cannot afford to remove and replace them so they try to improve existing housing and have introduced self-help schemes:

1. Self-help schemes in Rocinha.

- Breeze-block construction
- Electricity pirated from overhead supply
- First floor under construction
- Adjacent house
- Ground floor
- Doorway
- Unpaved road
- Pile of sand and bricks ready for building

Fig 2.19 Self-help housing

2. New transport routes, e.g. tunnels through the solid crystalline Serra do Mar mountain.

3. Building of new suburbs, e.g. Barra de Tuca, to create more housing.

4. Improved primary health care.

5. Long term, the best solution is to reduce migration to the cities by helping to spread development and wealth to rural areas; although this has proven almost impossible to achieve.

Quick Test

1. For any named developing city you have studied, describe measures taken to improve the quality of life in shanty towns.

Recent developments or changes in a developed world city

You must learn a **specific case study** in detail and be able to apply it to questions in the SQA exam. Look at each sector of your named city and ensure you have named examples for any recent (within 30 years) changes.

You may choose any world city, not just in Scotland. Major international events may influence change within a particular area of a city, for example the London

Fig 2.20 Construction in London's East End for the Olympics

2012 Olympics actioned great change in London's East End. However, here we look at changes in Scotland's central belt.

A tale of two cities: urban change in central Scotland

Fig 2.21 A tale of two cities: urban change in central Scotland

Glasgow – change in the C.B.D.	Recent developments in the rural/urban fringe	Edinburgh – change in the inner city

• Pedestrianisation, e.g. in Buchanan Street and Argyle Street
 	
• Upgrading of C.B.D. open space, e.g. George Square
 	
• Diversification of city employment – a much greater emphasis on the tourist industry (significance of city break holidays) leading to increased bed accommodation in new C.B.D. hotels (Hilton, Radisson)
 	
• Alteration of C.B.D. road network – one-way streets (around George Square), use of bus lanes to discourage use of private transport and encourage use of public transport
 	
• Renovation and redevelopment of many C.B.D. sites to provide modern hi-tech office space (e.g. Lloyds TSB, Direct Line etc.)
 	
• 24/7 use of the city centre (e.g. Cineworld in Renfrew Street)
 	
• High-profile shops to attract more customers, e.g. the Apple Store
 	
• New covered shopping centres, e.g. Buchanan Galleries
	• As both Edinburgh and Glasgow experience urban sprawl, the cities are growing across the central belt
	
	• Recent changes include:
	  – New housing estates
	  – Out-of-town shopping complexes e.g. Straiton or Braehead
	  – Park and ride complexes
	  – Development of tertiary and quaternary industrial estates, e.g. RBS at Gogarburn
		• Decline of old industry → areas cleared for new tertiary industries, e.g. leisure complex Fountain Park
		
		• Redevelopment of brownfield sites, e.g. Sainbury's between Gorgie Road and Westfield Road
		
		• Environmental landscaping – e.g. Canning Street
		
		• Clean up of Edinburgh Canal – now used for leisure e.g. Re-Union Canal Boats
		
		• Gentrification of area around the Union Canal – new luxury flats, new cafés and restaurants opened, e.g. Zizzi at Edinburgh Quay
		
		• Regeneration of housing, e.g. Gardner's Crescent
		
		• Improved transport links e.g. the Western Approach Road

EXAM TIP

Look at each sector of your named city and ensure that you have named examples for any changes that have happened within the last 30 years.

Quick Test

1. List five recent changes that have taken place in an inner city area of a city you have studied.

2. For a named city you have studied in a developed country, give reasons for the main changes that have taken place in the city centre shopping area over the last 30 years.

Changing countryside in the EU

There are over 500 million people living in the EU. 75 million live and work in rural areas, making farming and rural industries a key part of the economy. The EU produces huge quantities of agricultural and other primary products. Many millions of people depend on the land, or on processing land-based products, for a living. Foodstuffs account for 6.8% of EU exports at a value of over 116 billion euros.

EXAM TIP

Make use of detailed diagrams like the one in this section by extracting the information contained in the annotations. Converting the information into another form, such as a flow chart or before and after list, is a good method for learning and revising for exams.

Le Midi in the past

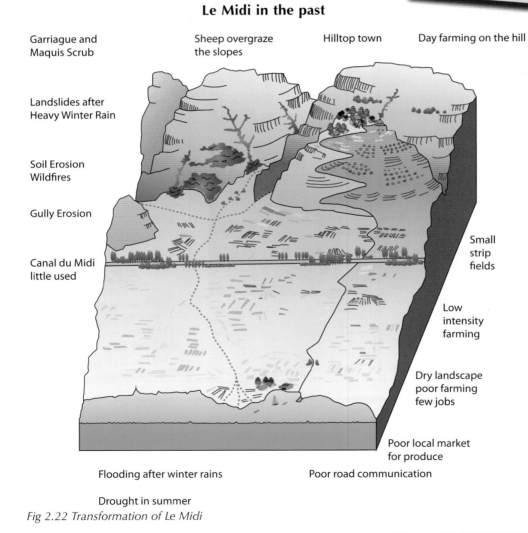

Garriague and Maquis Scrub

Sheep overgraze the slopes

Hilltop town

Day farming on the hill

Landslides after Heavy Winter Rain

Soil Erosion Wildfires

Gully Erosion

Canal du Midi little used

Small strip fields

Low intensity farming

Dry landscape poor farming few jobs

Poor local market for produce

Flooding after winter rains

Poor road communication

Drought in summer

Fig 2.22 Transformation of Le Midi

How is farming changing in the EU

The diagram shows changes in the landscape of Southern France and exemplifies how many rural areas in developed countries (like those in the EU) have been through a great transformation from old-style farming to modern agribusiness. People living in rural areas have seen their economy improve along with roads and towns. They have benefited from better-performing farming industries that are able to move goods to distant markets and from new industries that provide local jobs and improve the economy.

DID YOU KNOW?

Fewer and fewer people live in the countryside in Europe. This is called rural depopulation. Rural areas experience poorer economic conditions than towns and have less social and transport infrastructure.

Le Midi today

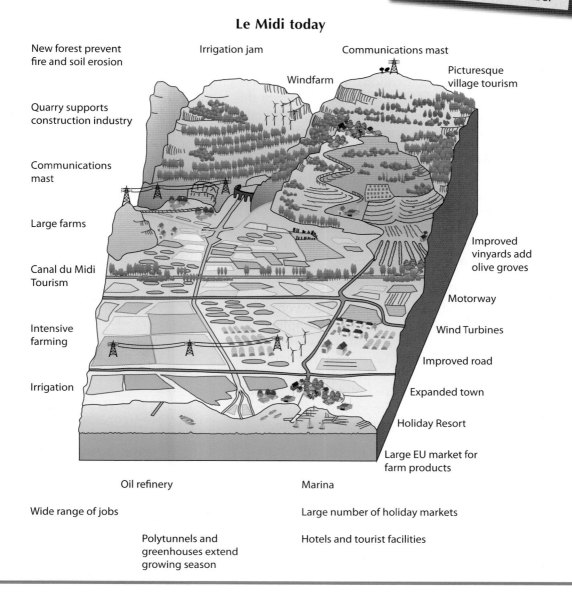

New forest prevent fire and soil erosion

Irrigation jam

Communications mast

Windfarm

Picturesque village tourism

Quarry supports construction industry

Communications mast

Large farms

Canal du Midi Tourism

Intensive farming

Irrigation

Improved vinyards add olive groves

Motorway

Wind Turbines

Improved road

Expanded town

Holiday Resort

Large EU market for farm products

Oil refinery

Marina

Wide range of jobs

Large number of holiday markets

Polytunnels and greenhouses extend growing season

Hotels and tourist facilities

Modern factors affecting farming

There are a number of factors at work that affect modern farming.

The Common Agricultural Policy (CAP)

This is a policy across the EU that supports farmers and helps to maintain stable prices to guarantee the income that farmers get for their products. EU policy also regulates aspects of farming, such as animal welfare, the use of genetically modified (GM) crops and what chemicals and fertilisers are safe to use on farms. For example, the EU has banned certain practices, such as keeping young cattle in veal crates. Farmers use set-aside land to prevent over-production of certain crops in return for guaranteed prices and payments.

GM crops

Genetically modified crops are a controversial issue. Manipulating plant genes allows certain beneficial characteristics of one organism or plant to be transferred artificially to another (genetic modification). This can increase crop yields or improve resistance to disease, pest or drought. Many people object to this arguing that it might have dangerous effects that impact on the environment and the effects of genetic modification may 'escape' and spread into non-modified crops or the the natural environment.

Organic farming

This is a specialised form of farming that avoids using such things as artificial fertilizers and pesticides and other agri-chemicals. Instead, more traditional methods or ecologically sensitive techniques are used to produce crops and livestock products such as organic vegetables and fruit, organic beef and organic milk and cheese. These products attract a higher price in supermarkets and are favoured by many people who wish to reduce their impact on the environment.

Diversification

Diversification is when farmers use other ventures to support their farming income. For example, some farms set up farm shops and restaurants and/ or have visitor areas. Other farms may have tourist-related activities or outdoor activities, such as off-road driving. Farms may lease holiday cottages or provide 'on the farm' accommodation. Wind farm development may also generate extra income.

Fig 2.23 Farm shop

Biofuels

One way of generating new income is to produce biofuels, which are used in special power stations or in regular generating stations as a substitute for fossil fuels. Farmers may grow fast-growing trees, such as willow, which can be cropped, or may grow oil-producing plants for bio-diesel. This industry allows farmers to diversify and also to be involved in carbon capture schemes favoured by governments anxious to reduce the effects of global warming.

New technology

The diagram of Southern France on page 63 shows how farming has become increasingly mechanised and uses much more control in the environment. Computerised systems, such as the use of GPS for managing field operations or for managing animal feeding, are typical of modern hi-tech farming. Production can be increased using water management systems that provide irrigation and drainage and through the use of poly-tunnels and environmental control systems.

Fig 2.24 New technology helps improve efficiency on farms

Government policy

Governments regulate and support their farming industries. In the UK, for example, the Department for Food and Rural Affairs (DeFRA) supports farming and rural communities. The Scottish Rural Development Programme does a similar job. Governments regulate farming practices and provide subsidies and support for farmers and rural industries. For example, in the UK there are laws covering animal welfare and the use of methods like GM crops. Fuel for farm vehicles is taxed at a lower rate. Governments provide money for research into agriculture. Disease control is mandatory, to prevent diseases such as foot and mouth disease, bovine TB and plant pests and diseases such as ash dieback and Colorado beetle infestation of potatoes.

Quick Test

1. What is the CAP of the European Union?
2. What are the disadvantages of using GM crops and why do some governments ban the import of GM crops from other countries such as the USA?
3. How can modern farming protect the environment?
4. How is foot and mouth disease or bovine TB controlled in Britain?

Brazil developing the Amazon

Brazil has a population of over 200 million people, with about 25 million living in the Amazon Region. In 1960, only 2 million people lived in this challenging environment so there is clearly major population pressure on the Earth's largest area of surviving equatorial rainforest.

What are the pressures on Amazonia?

Brazil currently has a National Income per head of $11,000 which is low compared to developed countries like the UK, where it is almost $36,000. Wealth in Brazil is not equally distributed across the country. The rich south-east region, dominated by large industrial cities and the rich agricultural heartland of the nation, generates over 56% of the national wealth. The poorest region is the north-east (sometimes referred to the Sertao), and contains the poorest district of all – the Caatinga. Brazil has a national policy to try to develop the country's resources, particularly those in the underdeveloped Amazonian region.

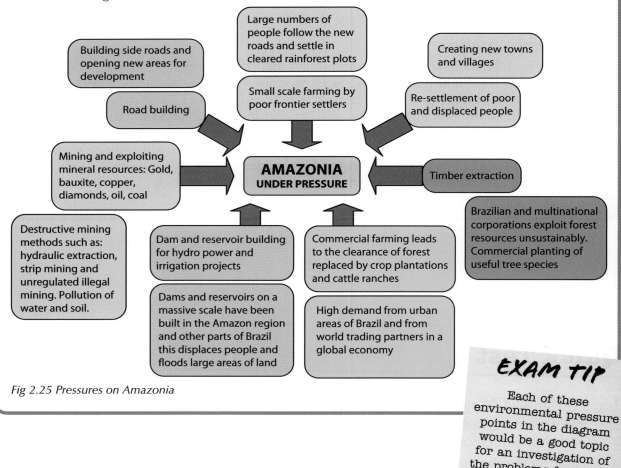

Fig 2.25 Pressures on Amazonia

EXAM TIP

Each of these environmental pressure points in the diagram would be a good topic for an investigation of the problems facing the Amazon rainforest.

The pressures diagram shows some of the main environmental pressure points facing Amazonia. With 20% of the rainforest cut down and being exploited, the threat to the environment has drawn international attention. These figures, calculated from satellite observations, show the pace of change:

Forest degradation 2007–2010 (Thousands of Hectares)				
	2007	**2008**	**2009**	**2010**
Amazonas	257	412	181	459
Mato Grosso	8951	12 987	8486	2502
Para	3899	8264	1558	3499
Rondonia	412	643	232	315
Amazonia	15 983	27 413	13 301	7508

Why is the Amazon under pressure?

The pressures have been created by the need for development to improve the economy and to help poor landless or displaced people from areas like the drought-affected north-east Brazil, as well as population growth. New settlers move into the region using the new roads. With or without government approval, they exploit forest timber reserves and make a living. Some people are given government land grants, while others who have migrated in as squatters work as subsistence farmers on small plots of cleared forest land to grow crops and keep animals.

Large dam-building projects like the Tucurui Dam or the new Belo Monte Dam displaces people, and those in other areas like the Sertao of the north-east region, have been displaced and encouraged to migrate to Amazonia.

Large mining companies are given licences by the government to prospect and exploit mineral and energy resources in the region. This supplies the Brazilian economy and generates export income. Similarly, multinational companies wish to exploit timber resources and ship them to developed countries to provide building materials and paper supplies. Multinational and national food processing companies use cleared land to grow cash crops such as coffee, fruit or palm oils. Cattle ranching helps meet the demand for meat and processed meat products like corned beef sold in supermarkets.

The growing south-east region and its towns and cities need cheap electricity for industry and for domestic supply. The Amazon River and its major tributaries provide this, but at the cost of losing forest areas to flooding.

Quick Test

1. Which region of Brazil shows the greatest amount of rainforest clearance?
2. Which is the poorest region of Brazil?

Sustainable development in Brazil

Can the rainforests be developed sustainably?

In the last 100 years, whole areas of the world have seen their forests cut down and lost to farming, urban development and industrial use. Population pressure in Indonesia, Malaysia and large areas of South-East Asia have seen their forests disappear, placing animals like the orangutan and other wildlife onto the endangered species list. Forest is replaced by industrial plantations producing food crops for export, industrial crops like rubber, or oil palm for food processing and industry. Urban development in industrialising countries spreads onto forested areas.

African forests have been similarly exploited and the rich forest environment may be replaced by scrub and secondary growth. This has had a major impact on wildlife, for example on the island of Madagascar where habitat destruction has resulted in many of its unique wildlife species, such as lemurs, being threatened with extinction. In India and Pakistan the remaining tiger population is now largely confined to natural reserves that are also under pressure from farmers and poachers. Without policies for preserving and developing forest resources sustainably, there is a chance that even the remaining forest areas have a limited future.

Why should equatorial and tropical forests be preserved?

Maintaining a healthy planet requires biodiversity. Natural systems tend to work on a feedback loop system so that upsetting the balance of nature is likely to have consequences down the line. Large-scale forest clearance by burning causes increased carbon dioxide levels in the atmosphere and contributes to climate change. Managing forests by clearing and thinning them and allowing secondary growth can cause large-scale bush fires, which in turns creates pollution of the atmosphere. Fires also threaten newly developed urban and industrial areas.

Fig 2.26 Forest clearance in the Amazon rainforest

Globalisation means that demands for supermarket foods and confectionary generates conflict as conservationists and local people object to new areas being developed for commercial farming. Conflicts are played out through the media and on the Internet as even small campaigns can undermine products. For example a campaign aimed at Nestle's Kit Kat because of oil palm planting in Indonesia was effective in changing company and government policy.

Major projects such as dams, mining schemes and agricultural developments do not always favour local people. Many are displaced and lose their land, jobs are often fewer than anticipated and go to incomers and people with technical skills. Other jobs are often unskilled and low paid and lead to exploitation of workers. Alternative opportunities, such as eco-tourism development or local sustainable schemes based on forest resources, are lost to multinational corporations or government agencies with dubious green credentials.

Forest area resources in remote districts can lead to political instability as rebel groups target mining sites to exploit mineral resources and finance revolutionary activity. Sierra Leone, Liberia, Rwanda and the Congo have all experienced this type of exploitation, and blood diamonds or illegal gold find their way onto the international markets. This often finances further terrorism and denies countries development money.

Sustainability options

The solution to the development versus rainforest conservation argument is difficult when it is clear how important development is to the Brazilian people, particularly the poor. The Brazilian Government has created a national parks authority, IBAMA, which not only administers 50 national parks but also looks after a wide range of natural, heritage and ecological reserves.

Carbon capture/replacement schemes have been put in place to develop long-term use of the forests. Many world conservation bodies, partner governments and commercial organisations have invested in rainforest conservation in Brazil. WWF and other agencies such as the UN environment programme have been involved in projects aimed at developing conservation strategies.

Major developments have met with international protests. The Monte Belo Dam project has been challenged in the Brazilian courts; conservationists have questioned the role of the World Bank in financing schemes like this that are likely to cause destruction of the natural environment. Indigenous peoples and local residents form pressure groups that raise concerns in Brazil and abroad. Consumer pressure can be effective in encouraging sustainable production. Fair trade schemes, sustainable source schemes for tropical timber and international agreements such as the CITES restrictions on the animal and animal products trade all contribute to a more sustainable future.

Quick Test

1. What is a plantation?
2. What are blood diamonds?
3. Why is it important to restrict the trade in rare animal products?
4. Why is fair trade a good thing?

Investigating Brazil's environmental issues

Investigations

At many points in your N5 Geography course you will be expected to conduct investigations or research essays and presentations. You will be given options for topics to study and follow at more depth. The rainforest and conservation issue in Brazil is one of international importance because these forests are the largest expanse of this natural system remaining in the world, which makes this fertile territory for investigations.

Making a start – sample where, why, what, when, how questions

1. Draw up a list of key questions about Brazil and its rainforests to develop your background knowledge of Brazil.

2. Collect and study maps, diagrams and images of Brazil: its cities and its natural environment.

3. Collect development statistics and others to compare against UK statistics.

4. Find 10 'did you know facts' about Brazil and Amazonia.

5. Design a series of search questions and research phrases relating to conservation and environmental issues. Find what issues are going on today. Look at the effects of past projects to find out whether they were successful.

6. Ask questions that relate to people affected by developments.

7. Identify conservation bodies working in the field.

Fig 2.27 Rio de Janeiro, Brazil

8. Investigate alternatives to proposed developments and follow up conservation schemes run by charities and other agencies.

Laying out a presentation

Presentations take many forms in Geography. One thing they have in common is the use of maps, diagrams, photos and graphic items. Collecting a range of these will enable you to add visual interest to your presentation but will also provide valuable resources to support your analysis of the issue. The following list gives a few suggestions.

- Maps: political, physical, climate, vegetation, economic activity, road and transport network, population density.
- Diagrams: model diagrams, cross sections, rainforest structure.
- Photographs: projects, satellite images, people involved, companies.
- Graphs: climate; population and development statistics; regional data for cross comparison; showing change over time.

Once you have a range of items work out their logical order and how you intend to use them in the presentation or report. All graphics should be processed and added to for added value. This means re-drawing and adapting, labelling and annotating, and turning raw data into meaningful graphs.

Presentation structure

Plan a logical structure for your presentation. Work out what you are trying to tell your audience and a logical sequence. If you are trying to be convincing, build to a conclusion using logical steps to be sure your audience stays with you. Consider how and when you use graphics to support your case. Develop initial impact by designing a short snappy introduction. Lay out you argument in advance. Present a balanced view by examining and criticising the arguments of both sides. Come to conclusions along the way and give your reasons for them. Summarise at the end the main points and draw your main conclusion.

Write up you first draft and read it over so you can edit it. Ask the key question (is this my own work?). Complete your final draft and check it over for remaining typos and mistakes.

What is climate change?

Climate change refers to a significant and lasting change in long-term weather patterns over periods of time ranging from decades to millions of years. It may be a change in average weather conditions, or in the distribution of weather statistics around the average conditions (i.e. more or fewer extreme weather events). Climate change is often confused with global warming as there has been a general increase in average global temperatures in the last 150 years.

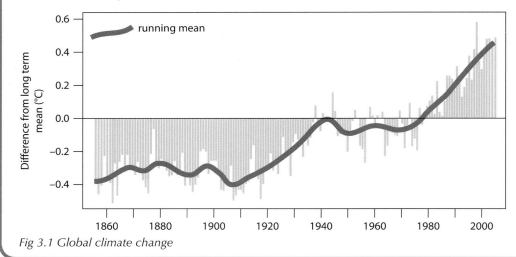

Fig 3.1 Global climate change

Evidence for climate change

EXAM TIP

You can find useful information on climate change on the Met Office website: http://www.metoffice.gov.uk/climate-change/guide/what-is-it.

- Long-term evidence (1000s years): ice core analysis.
- Medium-term evidence (100s years): historical records, glacial retreat, dendro-chronology.
- Recent evidence (decades): changes in biodiversity, climate records, sea ice limits.

Fig 3.2 Melting glaciers, Iceland

Causes of climate change

Greenhouse gases are produced naturally but are added to by human activity. This causes the **enhanced greenhouse effect,** which is believed to be the main reason behind the current pattern of climate change.

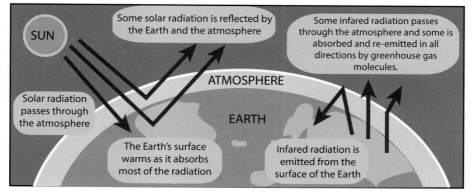

Fig 3.3 The greenhouse effect

Physical (natural) causes	Human (anthropogenic) causes
Changing output of solar radiation – changes in the amount of energy given out by the sun over time.	**Fossil fuels** – Increased consumption of coal, oil and natural gas has increased the amount of CO_2 in the atmosphere.
Volcanic eruptions – and the amount of volcanic dust particles which enter the atmosphere as a result. Dust acts as a blanket shielding the Earth from incoming solar radiation and leads to a decrease in temperature.	**Deforestation** – especially the burning of tropical rainforests adds to the concentration of CO_2 and decreases the amount used by plants in photosynthesis.
Wobble roll and stretch theory (the Milankovitch Theory) – changes in the movement of the Earth's angle of tilt, its orbit around the Sun and the gravitational pull of the Sun and the Moon all change the amount of energy the Earth receives from the Sun, therefore influencing climatic temperature.	**Increased methane** – this comes from flatulent cattle, rice padi fields and waste in landfill sites, which are all caused by an increase in the population. **Increased output of nitrous oxides** – these are from agricultural fertilisers and pesticides.
Changing oceanic circulation – for example, **El Nino**/La Nina.	**CFCs (chloroflourocarbons)** – these leak from old fridges and can remain in the atmosphere for up to 400 years. They add to the enhanced greenhouse effect.

EXAM TIP

Refer to specific greenhouse gases and how they are produced.

Quick Test

1. Describe the physical factors which have led to climate change.
2. Explain how human activity has influence climate change.

Consequences of climate change

Many effects of climate change are negative and will have the greatest effect on developing countries and the world's poorest people, although some potential impacts are positive.

Negative effects of climate change

- **Environmental** – rising sea levels, coastal flooding, loss of habitats, some islands uninhabitable (e.g. in the Maldives), an increase in extreme weather events such as European heat waves, increased droughts in Africa and severe hurricanes in the USA, the disappearance of the polar ice cap.
- **Social** – tropical diseases (e.g. malaria) moving into temperate latitudes, climate wars fought over precious food and water.
- **Economic** – a loss of locally important economic activities such as skiing in the Alps.

Fig 3.4 Hurricane Sandy caused more than $68 billion worth of damage in October 2012. Increased hurricanes can be an effect of climate change

Positive effects of climate change

Social – Warming of northern latitudes leading to increased tourism, for example, warmer Scottish summers.

Economic – Changing agricultural patterns e.g. maize grown in Scotland instead of potatoes; improved crop yields as warmer temperatures ensure longer growing periods. This can lead to a reduced level of dependency on other nations if countries become self-sufficient in terms of food supplies.

> **EXAM TIP**
>
> Make reference to positive and negative effects on the economy and the environment in both developed and developing countries. Use up-to-date named examples.

Fig 3.5 Warmer temperatures improve crop yields

Reducing the effects of climate change

You should be able to distinguish between strategies that lead to both prevention (avoiding climate change) and mitigation (making the effects less severe).

- **Local strategies**, such as 'Reduce, Reuse, Recycle' (household recycling), reducing food miles, cycle to school and switching off lights when not in use.
- **National strategies** (government initiatives), such as road tax for 'gas guzzlers', low-emission vehicle incentives and carbon reduction initiatives in homes such as boiler upgrades, loft insulation and photovoltaic panels.
- **International strategies**, such as geo-engineering, improved technology, United Nations agreements/regulations concerning climate change, the Intergovernmental Panel on Climate Change (IPCC).

Quick Test

1. How can we reduce the effects of climate change?
2. What evidence is there that climate change is taking place?

Equatorial versus tundra environments

Tundra Areas Equatorial Areas

EXAM TIP

To describe any climate graph you need to include details such as highest and lowest temperatures, the range of temperature and highs and lows of annual precipitation. Also when these events occur in the year and whether there is any lengthy dry or wet season.

Equatorial (rainforest) environments

- **Location:** these are dense rainforest areas found in lowland areas 10 degrees either side of the Equator (0)

- Often described as the 'world's lungs' because of all the oxygen produced by the forests

- **Regions/countries with an equatorial rainforest climate:** Amazonia in Brazil, Peru, Indonesia, Colombia, Democratic Republic of Congo

- **Climate summary:**

Manaus, Brazil (Equatorial Climate)

■ Precipitation (mm) ● Daily Mean (°C)

- Total annual precipitation: 2286 mm

- Maximum temperature: 27°C

- Minimum temperature: 26°C

- Range of temperature (remember the difference between the max. and the min. temp): 1°C

- It is hot and wet all year round

Tundra environments

- **Location:** these are cold desert areas mostly found north of the Arctic Circle (66½ N)

- In Finnish, tundra literally means 'barren or treeless land'

- **Regions/countries with a tundra climate:** Northern Alaska, Northern Canada, Northern Russia (Siberia) and Northern Scandinavia

- **Climate summary:**

Inuvick, Northern Canada (Tundra Climate)

■ Precipitation (mm) ● Daily Mean (°C)

Fig 3.6 Equatorial versus tundra environments

- Total annual precipitation: 250 mm

- Maximum temperature: 14°C

- Minimum temperature: −28°C

- Range of temperature: 42°C

- Very cold, dark, long winters

- Very short, light summers

- The amount of rain and snow are so low (<250 mm a year) that the tundra is classed as a desert

Equatorial vegetation

Section Through a Rainforest

A - The main forest canopy traps sunlight and rain | **B** - The tallest trees or emergents | **C** - Thousands of other plants are found here eg : orchids, creepers, fungi, ferns | **D** - The forest floor is dark and damp. Dead leaf layer | **E** - Thick layer of dead leaves or huncus. No grass, many decomposers

Top layer

Middle layer

Under canopy

Shrub layer

Fig 3.7 Equatorial vegetation

- All the trees are broadleaved evergreens because the high temperatures and evenly distributed precipitation through the year allow continuous growth.
- The canopy is a dense layer of leaves allowing very little light to penetrate to the forest floor. This canopy has an abundance of flowers and fruit.
- Buttress roots support the very tall trees or 'emergents' (50–60 m high).
- Without the rainforest canopy the soils become infertile very quickly as the heavy rainfall soon leaches all the nutrients.

Tundra vegetation

Tundra Landscape will Common Vegetation

A - Lichens on bare rocks | **B** - Heather, bilberry (Plants grow close to the ground because there are strong cold winds) | **C** - Dwarf trees eg : willow (Trees have short roots as only the top layer of soil is not permanently frozen) | **D** - Bog cotton (Found in marshy areas in the short tundra summer)

Fig 3.8 Tundra vegetation

- The growing season is very short (about 2 months).
- In the short summer only the surface soil thaws (top 50 cms) and the subsoil remains frozen (permafrost).
- This leaves the soil waterlogged in summer and there it has a lack of nutrients.
- The vegetation has to survive extreme cold, biting winds and a moisture deficit.

Equatorial wildlife

- Animal and bird life in the rainforest are abundant due to the availability of food and shelter.
- Equatorial rainforests are the most diverse ecosystem on Earth and have two thirds of all the world's wildlife species, e.g. monkeys, sloths, jaguars, parrots.

Tundra wildlife

- The tundra has fewer species of plants than any other ecosystem.
- Conditions are very difficult for the species that live here, e.g. caribou, arctic wolf, musk ox.

Quick Test

1. Which two climatic characteristics mean that there is continuous growth in equatorial rainforest environments?

2. Why are tundra areas classed as deserts?

3. What is the direct result of removing the rainforest canopy?

Misuse of equatorial rainforests

The broken nutrient cycle

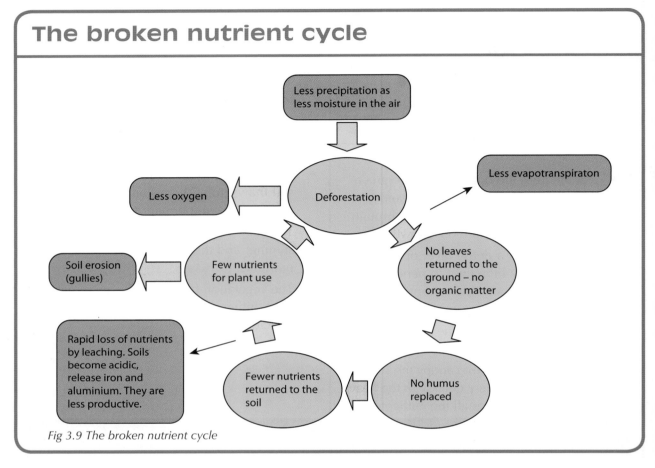

Fig 3.9 The broken nutrient cycle

Causes of deforestation

- **Logging** – large areas of rainforest are being clear felled for hardwoods, such as mahogany and rosewood.
- **Plantation farming** – areas are cleared for the cultivation of cacao, soya and coffee.
- **Cattle ranching** – large areas are cleared for the production of beef. Most ranches only last 10 years as the grass quality decreases because of the poor soils.
- **Construction of hydroelectric power (HEP) schemes** – large areas of the forest are flooded for the generation of electricity.
- **Roads/communications** – the population of Amazonia is growing and so are the number of developments and these all need access by a network of roads.
- **Mineral extraction** – Amazonia is rich in mineral deposits, e.g. gold, bauxite and iron ore, which attract mining companies.

Effects of deforestation

DID YOU KNOW?
Human deforestation breaks the natural cycle within the equatorial rainforest.

- With a lack of tree cover, run-off and soil erosion increases.
- This leads to gullying, flooding, landslides and increased sedimentation in rivers.
- Habitat loss means the reduction of the number of animal and plant species (the biodiversity) able to survive in the rainforests.
- Loss of an invaluable resource of raw materials for medical drugs.
- If the rainforest is cleared by burning, the carbon dioxide released contributes to global warming.
- The trees convert carbon dioxide into food and release oxygen; with fewer trees this process is less effective.
- The indigenous Indians lose their lands and way of life as they are forced to live in a smaller area of rainforest.

Possible solutions to deforestation

EXAM TIP
Practice drawing quick spider diagrams for the causes, effects and possible solutions of deforestation.

- **Banning logging** – this is difficult to enforce as the forest is very dense and difficult to patrol. It can just lead to the smuggling of illegal timber.
- **Different logging methods** – this is more realistic. Selective logging means only trees with a certain thickness and the least important trees are felled. There are also controls on the use of heavy machinery.
- **Satellite imagery** – vast areas can be monitored with satellite imagery to show the extent of deforestation. However, not all countries have the money or technical knowledge to implement this technology.
- **Conservation and replanting** – this can be difficult on the poor-quality soils, and competition from grasses mean the tree seedlings often die.
- **Certification** – this involves marking the wood with a barcode so that the wood can be sourced from 'stump to store shelf'. This means customers can make informed choices and choose to buy sustainable, or 'eco-friendly', wood.

Quick Test

1. What is deforestation?
2. What impact does rainforest deforestation have on medical advances worldwide?
3. Why might trying to impose a worldwide ban on logging in equatorial rainforest be difficult to enforce?
4. Identify four causes of deforestation.

Misuse of the tundra

Although the tundra is a region of low population density it has many natural resources. Many developed countries would like to exploit these resources and in Alaska the Americans are already busy doing so, but as you can see from the articles below this is often at the expense of the natural environment:

Alaska hit by 'massive' oil spill

On March 2nd 2006 an oil spill was discovered on the Prudhoe Bay oil field. Experts estimated that up to 267 000 gallons (one million litres) of crude oil had leaked from a corroded pipeline in the northern part of the Alaskan state. The spill was described as 'a catastrophe' by environmentalists. Alaska was still recovering from the Exxon Valdez shipping disaster in 1989 when 11 million gallons

(42 million litres) of oil was washed on to the Alaskan coast.

PROPOSED PEBBLE MINE, BRISTOL BAY, ALASKA

In October 2012 a proposal by a transnational corporation for a copper and gold mine was put forward. This region is an area of fragile tundra on the shores of Bristol Bay. It will also be close to two of Alaska's beluga whale populations including the last 340 belugas of the Cook Inlet. Environmentalists have demanded that the mining giant, Anglo American Corporation, leave Bristol Bay and the beluga whales alone. Then an Environmental Impact Assessment (completed in April 2013) has also claimed that the toxic waste that would be produced by the mine and released into the Bay would directly threaten the salmon farming industry which is so important to the Alaskan economy.

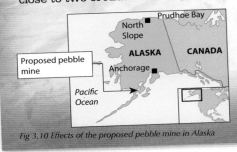

Fig 3.10 Effects of the proposed pebble mine in Alaska

Effects on the tundra landscape
- Disturbance of the delicate ecosystem
- Disruption to wildlife habitat and migration patterns, e.g. caribou migration
- Pollution of the land and water courses
- Abandoned waste
- Destruction of one of the last of the world's wilderness areas

The tundra is a very fragile ecosystem in delicate balance. Once disturbed by human activity it may take many years to re-establish.

Positive effects of the proposed pebble mine	Negative effects of the proposed pebble mine
• Creation of jobs. • Provide tax revenues for the state of Alaska. • Reduce dependence of the US on foreign sources of raw materials.	• Decline of fish populations. • Contamination of sea water by waste water. • Large amounts of waste rock material. • Giant open cast mine cut into the tundra landscape. • Disruption of local drainage basins and river flow. • Disruption to wildlife in this currently wild and undeveloped landscape. • Beluga whale population under threat. • The development will require the building of miles of roads and bridges.

Quick Test

1. Name two activities that threaten tundra environments.
2. Identify three positive effects of development on the tundra environment.

Environmental hazards case study: Bangladesh

In this section you will choose a topic such as environmental hazards and use your geographical knowledge and skills to research in depth a specific line of enquiry. From your research you must produce a presentation to demonstrate your knowledge and understanding and your ability to use a range of geographical and presentation skills.

What are environmental hazards?

Natural hazards come in many forms and are different from natural disasters.

- Natural hazards are either geomorphological occurrences relating to floods, earthquakes, volcanoes, landslides, tsunami or meteorological phenomena such as hurricanes, storms, floods, forest fires and droughts.
- Natural disasters occur when people are overtaken by the natural hazards listed above. This will involve loss of life, injury and destruction of property. It will have an effect on future economic development and prosperity that extends beyond the immediate effects of the disaster involved.

Case study: Why does Bangladesh flood and why do natural disasters occur here?

Fig 3.11 Bangladesh floods: natural hazard and natural disasters

- Heavy monsoon, snowfall on the High Himalayas produces melt water that causes flooding lower down the river basin
- Forest clearance in Nepal, Bhutan and The Himalaya increases flooding and flood risk by rivers
- Cleared land prone to soil erosion. Flash floods carry soil down to the main river channel
- Irrigation schemes and dams reduce the amount of silt that reaches the delta. This increases the flood risk lower down
- Cleared land on slopes looses its fertility and soil is blown or washed away to affect other land in the area
- Silt is carried down to the flood plains
- Every year about 18-20% of Bangladesh floods a killing at least 5,000 people and flooding a million houses
- High population numbers, high population density on the fertile flood plains
- Forests help control runoff and protects against flooding
- Forest burning lays waste large areas of land
- Forests cleared and hillsides terraced to grow crops
- Much of Bangladesh is low lying less than 1 m above sea level. It is made up of the delta of two major river systems – The Ganges and the Brahmaputra
- Tropical cyclones (Hurricanes) drive into the Bay of Bengal. Storm surges push flood water up the river and over the low lying land
- New land is created in the delta from silt delivered by the rivers. Many people live on these Islands
- Global warming produces higher sea levels and storms of greater intensity threatening low lying Bangladesh

Figure 3.11 shows why there is a flood hazard and why there are corresponding flood disasters in Bangladesh. With much of the area lying below tidal and river flood levels, over 75% of the land area is at risk in a severe flood event. Bangladesh has a population of 151 million, living in a land where 18% of the land floods every year. The statistics below make sombre reading.

Bangladesh flooding statistics 1980–2012	
Number of flooding events	234
Number of people killed	191 836
Average number of fatalities per year	6188
Number of people affected by flooding	323 480 264
Average number affected per year	10 434 847
Economic damage	$17 072 500 000
Average economic damage per year	$550 726 000

Fig 3.12 Bangladesh flooding statistics, 1980–2012

Beyond the flooding, millions of people are affected by the waterborne diseases associated with flooding, such as cholera, typhoid fever and diarrhoeal diseases.

Managing the risks

The government, local authorities and people of Bangladesh live with the hazard and are able to risk assess and plan responses to potential disasters:

- Hazard maps can be produced using GIS. (These are available to students on the Internet.)
- Monitoring systems can be put in place to track tropical cyclones threatening the Bay of Bengal using meteorological satellites.
- Early warning systems give people time to move to higher ground, education and public information systems raise public awareness.
- Flood shelters are provided in relatively safe locations.
- Emergency plans, food stores and relief stores are created. Safe (bottled) water is provided on a temporary basis after a flood.
- Water purification systems are put into operation.

Fig 3.13 Floodwaters surrounding houses in Dhaka, Bangladesh

Bangladesh is a poor country, and it has a huge demand for farm land to support its population. This means, that while recognising the hazard and related risks, people live with the potential for disaster year by year.

Why is the risk and hazard increasing?

Environmental change is making the problems worse. Increasing global temperatures threaten to raise sea levels even further year by year. Global warming is predicted to increase the number and intensity of tropical storms. The upper basins of the Ganges and Brahmaputra rivers lie in India, Nepal, Tibet and Bhutan – beyond the control of the government and people of Bangladesh. There, forest clearance is accelerating the speed of run-off, increasing the flood risk. Management of the river by dams reduces the growth of the delta so less land is created at the seaward end of the system to protect the lowest lying areas.

The future

International cooperation must continue in order to manage the whole river basin and protect vulnerable populations. Grass roots organisations like the Chipko movement can reduce forest destruction in favour of more sustainable land use for the people in the Himalayas and the foothills above Bangladesh and the flood plain. Flood protection schemes can protect industrial and urban areas but are expensive to build and maintain.

Follow up

Either a) investigate some of the issues raised above or b) study one of the topics in the table below to develop your own investigation around the environmental hazards issue.

Environmental hazard	Case study sources
Earthquakes and tsunamis	• Fukushima earthquake Japan • South-East Asia tsunami • Christchurch earthquake • Any current earthquake in the news • Vulnerable places: San Francisco/California, Mexico City, Italy, Turkey, Alaska, China, Pakistan
Volcanoes	• Krakatoa • Andean volcanoes in Peru • Columbia • Montserrat and the West Indies • The Phillipines • Vesuvius – is Naples threatened? • Iceland and the threats to air travel in Europe
Flooding	• Bangladesh, India, Pakistan relating to forest clearance and monsoon rains • Mississippi River and the Tennessee Valley of the USA • Major European rivers such as the Danube or the Rhine • Flash floods and river floods in Britain, how are they managed?
Tropical storms	• Hurricanes in the Gulf of Mexico and Caribbean • Cyclones in Bangladesh • Typhoons in the South China Sea
Forest fires	• Australian forest fires – how are they caused and what effects do they have? • Mediterranean Europe • Rainforests ablaze in South-East Asia
Coastal flooding	• The effects of rising sea levels on low-lying land areas

Fig 3.14 Environmental hazard case studies

EXAM TIP

The issues in Bangladesh make an ideal individual study because there are a large number of contributing factors to its flood hazard and its increasing flood disaster risk.

Quick Test

1. What is a hazard map?
2. What is a typhoon?
3. Summarise the causes and effects of flooding in Bangladesh using the sources on these pages.
4. As a follow up, research the hazards and the disasters affecting Bangladesh.

Trade

Trade is the exchange of goods and services between countries. Trade is necessary as no country in the world is self-sufficient (i.e. supplies everything it needs). So countries have to:

- **Import** – buy goods they need from other countries.
- **Export** – sell goods they produce to other countries.
- **Have a positive balance of trade** – the difference in value between imports and exports.

If a country buys more than it sells, that country will have a trade deficit. If a country sells more than it buys it will have a trade surplus. If the imports equal exports then a country is said to have a balance of trade. World trade patterns are very important as they determine a country's economy and hence its level of development.

- Developed countries rely on the import of raw materials or primary goods, which they then process and turn into manufactured goods for export.
- Developing countries are still the main producers of primary goods, which they export, but they have to often import manufactured goods. The price a developing country is paid for a raw material or primary good is a fraction of the price paid for the manufactured good it is made into.
- Developed countries often have a trade surplus. Developing countries often have a trade deficit. However, the UK actually has a trade deficit and many countries in both the developed and the developing world are not really paying their way in terms of production but are instead mortgaging future production. The UK is currently paying £1 billion per week in interest on its debts.

However, developed and developing countries are interdependent of each other.

DID YOU KNOW?

Developing countries have only a small share of world trade and prices for goods are determined by the developed countries.

Newly industrialised countries

Newly industrialised countries (NICs) sit 'between' developing and developed status. They have growing economies and are experiencing rapid industrialisation, for example China, Brazil, India, Mexico, South Africa, Turkey and Malaysia.

EXAM TIP

Make sure you can identify the exports of at least two of these countries. An explanation of why these countries are changing is shown opposite.

The Clark-Fisher Model

This model shows that as a country's economy grows the relative importance of its three sectors (primary, secondary and tertiary) change.

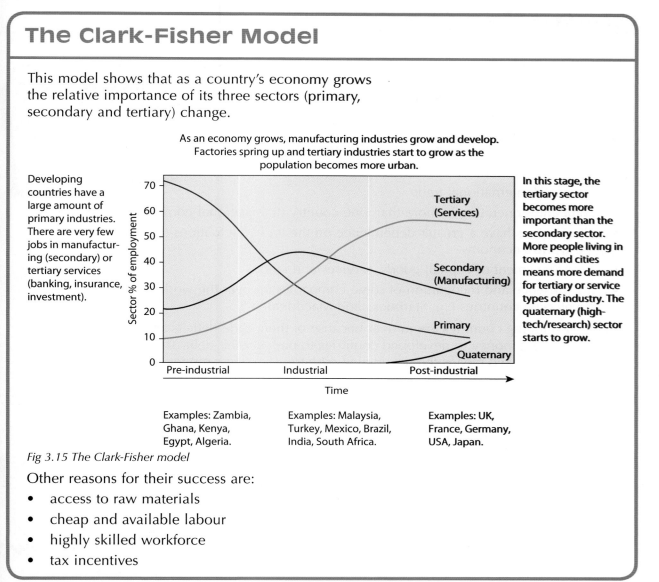

As an economy grows, manufacturing industries grow and develop. Factories spring up and tertiary industries start to grow as the population becomes more urban.

Developing countries have a large amount of primary industries. There are very few jobs in manufacturing (secondary) or tertiary services (banking, insurance, investment).

In this stage, the tertiary sector becomes more important than the secondary sector. More people living in towns and cities means more demand for tertiary or service types of industry. The quaternary (high-tech/research) sector starts to grow.

Examples: Zambia, Ghana, Kenya, Egypt, Algeria.

Examples: Malaysia, Turkey, Mexico, Brazil, India, South Africa.

Examples: UK, France, Germany, USA, Japan.

Fig 3.15 The Clark-Fisher model

Other reasons for their success are:

- access to raw materials
- cheap and available labour
- highly skilled workforce
- tax incentives

Quick Test

1. Explain the difference between imports and exports.
2. What is meant by the 'balance of trade'?
3. Why do developing countries often have a trade deficit?
4. Explain why developed and developing countries are 'interdependent'.

Globalisation

The world has become increasingly interconnected as a result of increased trade, telecommunications, the Internet and the exchange of cultures. This is referred to as 'globalisation'. Some of the world's biggest companies are no longer national but international (operating in many countries around the world).

EXAM TIP

Warning! This does not mean that globalisation is helping to close the gap between the rich and the poor.

Globalisation has meant:

- increased international trade
- companies operating in more than one country (transnational corporations or TNCs)
- all countries have a greater dependence on the trade fluctuations (up and downs) of the world's economy
- freer movement of capital, goods, services and labour
- the presence and recognition of some companies all over the world, even in developing countries e.g. Starbucks and Macdonald's

Many developing countries are in debt because of their trade deficits and they are actually paying money to developed countries to pay off their debt. This makes developed countries richer and means the developing countries have less money to invest in manufacturing, education and health care.

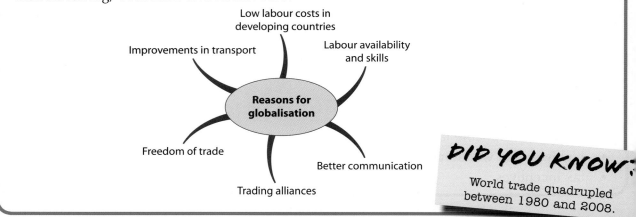

Low labour costs in developing countries

Improvements in transport

Labour availability and skills

Reasons for globalisation

Freedom of trade

Better communication

Trading alliances

DID YOU KNOW:

World trade quadrupled between 1980 and 2008.

Trading alliances

Some countries group together for economic reasons. Examples of trading alliances are the EU, NAFTA (North American Free Trade Association) and OPEC (Organisation of Petroleum Exporting Countries). Member states within a trading alliance gain certain benefits:

- No tariffs (import taxes) on goods traded between member states
- Free movement of labour
- All countries contribute money to the alliance and the resources of the member countries can be more evenly distributed
- Control may be put on the price of a raw material, for example oil by the OPEC alliance

Despite these alliances, developed countries still dominate world trade. In 2008 the five largest importers and exporters were Germany, USA, France and Japan. These have now been joined by China, which has pushed the UK into sixth place. These countries account for 81% of all trade.

Transnational corporations

A transnational corporation (TNC) is also called a multinational company. These TNCs often have headquarters in a developed country and increasingly factories in developing countries. Some examples of TNCs are Coca-Cola, Microsoft, Dell, Honda, Sony, Nestlé, Royal Dutch Shell and Vodafone. In the past, manufacturers and oil companies have been the largest corporations, but telecommunications are beginning to catch up. 75% of world trade is carried out by these corporations and their benefits to the developing world are often disputed. This table lists the advantages and disadvantages of TNCs to a developing country.

Advantages	Disadvantages
TNCs bring work and employ local labour.	The presence of TNCs encourages the local young people into factories rather than into education.
TNCs often pay higher than the national average.	Profits of the corporations go back to developed countries.
TNCs bring improvements to infrastructure e.g. roads and rail.	The number of local employees is actually quite low.
TNCs bring in other foreign investment.	The work of TNCs often has negative environmental impacts, for example oil spills in Nigeria.

Fig 3.16 Advantages and disadvantages of Transnational corporation

Quick Test

1. Give three reasons for globalisation.
2. Identify two benefits of forming a trading alliance.
3. Give two negative impacts of a TNC (Transnational Corporation) in a developing country.

The developing world fights back

Developing countries lose out on the value of a product by exporting them in their raw state rather than processing them. One solution to increase earnings is to tax these exported raw materials. This may make them less attractive on world markets but it would significantly increase the country's income.

Case study: Kenyan leather trade

Africa produces 15% of the world's cow hides and 25% of the world's goat and sheep skins. Yet its global share of leather production is only 2% because most of it is processed elsewhere. Here is how Kenya tried to address this:

The 1990s Kenyan Government reduced the taxes on leather goods coming into the country.

↓

This lead to a crisis as the Kenyan leather trade could not compete with the cheap imports.

↓

The Kenyan Government lost millions of pounds in revenue.

↓

In 2006, Kenya launched its Vision 2030 policy and an export tax was put on raw hides and skins.

↓

This meant that it was better for the hides and skins to be processed into leather in Kenya. Now between 96 and 98% of hides and skins were processed in Kenyan tanneries. This lead to higher export earnings, more jobs and better wages.

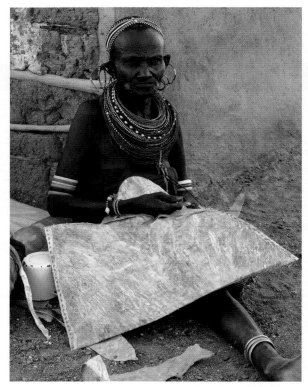

Fig 3.17 A Kenyan woman creates a bag from goat skin

Fair trade

Fair trade guarantees good prices for produce – usually raw materials such as bananas, coffee and cocoa – and this helps to create stability and benefits the whole community.

> **EXAM TIP**
>
> Pick a TNC such as Coca-Cola as a case study and look at where it is located worldwide, who are its trading partners and the positive and negative impacts it has on the developed and developing countries it operates from.

- Fair trade pays a guaranteed minimum price to the grower to protect them from world price fluctuations.

- At least 20% of the profit goes to the grower in an effort to cut out the middleman (the importer, e.g. UK supermarkets).

Fair trade products do cost more but shoppers need to understand that long-term this will reduce inequalities in world trade and help producers in developing countries.

'Fair Trade is about making sure people get their fair share of the pie. Nobody wants to buy something that was made by exploiting somebody else.'

Jerry Greenfield from Ben & Jerry's Ice Cream, 2010

Fig 3.18 Coffee is a popular fairtrade product

Quick Test

1. What is fair trade?

2. What percentage of the profit for the produce, e.g. bananas, goes to the grower/producer?

What is global tourism?

Global tourism is a multibillion pound industry that is one of the leading sources of income in the world and has a huge impact on the economic development of people, areas and individual countries.

In 2011 tourism generated an estimated global income of over US$ 2 trillion and employed over 98 million people worldwide. In 2012 this industry was scheduled to grow by 2.7%, increasing the income generated and the numbers of people employed. Tourism has a positive economic impact on both the developed and developing parts of the world and many countries see tourism as an important aspect of future development. Other figures released by the World Trade and Tourism Council suggest that tourism accounts for 9% of world GDP, 8% of jobs, 5% of investment and 5% of world export figures.

World tourism in figures (2012)

Leading tourism earners 2012		Fastest growing tourist economies 2012	
Country	Tourist income $US trillion	Country	% growth in travel and tourism
USA	1315.6	Thailand	15.6
China	643.4	Uganda	14.5
Japan	390.9	Uruguay	13.8
France	256.9	Hong Kong	12.6
Spain	222.6	Laos	12.3
Brazil	212.9	Namibia	11.8
Germany	189.5	Turkey	11.4
Italy	163.7	Singapore	11.2
United Kingdom	162.2	Antilles	10.6
Australia	145.5	Haiti	9.6

Fig 3.19 Leading tourist earners and fastest growing tourist economies, 2012

These figures show that developed countries generate the most income from tourism but developing countries figure in the boom in global tourism.

The impact of tourism

Although it plays an important part in economic development, tourism also has an effect on people and the environment. The key word with tourism is **sustainability**. If tourism is not managed effectively it may cause problems that limit its economic benefits and may even kill off tourism as the attractiveness of a tourist area declines through the impact of too many people.

What is the Butler Model of Tourism Growth?

The Butler Model of Tourism Growth uses the experience of tourism development in, for example, Europe since the 1960s, to identify how a tourist economy will develop and decline or re-invent itself in a sustainable way.

Stage 3 Success: The tourist industry develops to the point where it reaches its full potential with all its facilities working to full capacity. Little of the original natural environment is left and the lives of people in the area will have changed significantly along with traditional towns, villages and traditional lifestyles. The area loses its unique charms and becomes rather like the rest of the world (globalisation).

Stage 2 Growth/Development: Initial interest in the area grows and spreads through the media and by word of mouth. Special tourist infrastructure such as hotels, roads, airports and transport termini are built along with improvements to water and sewage provision. This all provides jobs and money for the economy.

Stage 1 Discovery: A new tourist area is identified by a small number of visitors based for example on its wildlife interest, its historic attractions, its potential for outdoor leisure pursuits, its special culture or its idyllic tourist attractions.

Fig 3.20 The Butler Model

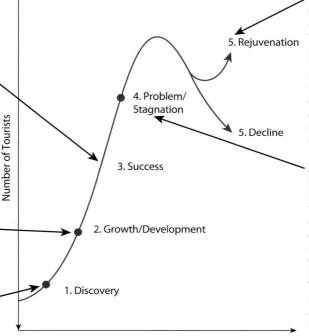

Stage 5 Rejuvenation or Decline? The tourist area has an option here to deal with the reasons for decline and invest money to re-brand and re-develop the area or continue with declining tourist income and falling employment.

Stage 4 Problem/Stagnation: People become bored with the area or the area becomes spoiled and visitors move on to newer developments elsewhere which are less spoiled by tourism. The tourist area goes into economic decline and the tourist facilities become jaded and in need of an upgrade.

EXAM TIP

In this section of the course it is important to choose case studies of tourist development and eco-tourism. Use the Internet to research a particular part of the world you are interested in. Why not choose a place you have visited on holiday and work out how much impact you and your family had on the economy and environment of the area? Questions like those in the Quick Test can be used (along with others) to focus your study.

Quick Test

1. Why is tourism important on a global scale?
2. How can success in developing a tourist area lead to problems?
3. What would be the effect of stagnation on a tourist area?

What impact does tourism have on an area?

Many people complain about the impact of tourism on an area and how it might spoil the very places that visitors come to see and enjoy. Eco-tourism might be defined as being all about people visiting environmentally sensitive areas, but if the visitors create problems for landscape, cultural features such as historic sites and wildlife, then tourism is not sustainable. Eco-tourism should be about visitors having little or no impact on the original environment and about management systems being put in place that achieve the vital tourist income but protect the environmentally sensitive area.

Managing tourism and related problems

Tourist activity	Problem caused	Management strategy
Large numbers of tourists visit an environmentally sensitive area	• Wildlife is disturbed and moves away • Trails and paths are developed • Accommodation puts demands on water and local fuel resources	• Designate national parks and nature reserves • Restrict access to reduced areas • Use renewable energy sources rather than local wood
Beach and coastal tourism	• Sprawling urban development along the coast • Sewage disposal and environmental pollution • Demands on water resources	• Develop planning guidelines to allow appropriate development • Build sewage disposal capacity • Conserve water supplies by recycling waste water • Protect sensitive coastal environments by creating marine reserves or restricting access to reefs for divers
Visiting historic sites	• Visitor numbers cause erosion on ancient buildings by footfall • Entering old buildings may damage wall paintings and artefacts	• Restrict access to fewer people • Build replicas of the original site such as Tutankhamen's tomb or the Lascaux caves and their paintings
Safari and wildlife experiences	• Visitors disturb wildlife and local people disrupting their 'natural' way of life • Animals are habituated to people being present and become a danger to locals and visitors	• Develop low impact visit strategies that keep a distance between people and the target wildlife • Restrict access maintaining off limit parts of reserves • Reduce hunting and camping in the field

Ski development	• Visitors generate demand for ski facilities and uplift (his can spoil sensitive mountain environments) • High demand for water and sewage infrastructure creates supply and disposal problems	• Develop environment guidelines for ski development • Conduct environmental impact studies and ecological surveys • Assess new avalanche risks caused by tourist development
Waste management	• Visitors produce large amounts of rubbish and waste in environmentally sensitive areas that may not be disposed of appropriately	• Provide public education and guidelines that reduce packaging • Recycle waste and remove it to proper facilities • Reduce reuse and recycle campaigns

Fig 3.21 Managing tourism

What is mass tourism?

Some areas like the Spanish Costas, Florida, and major ski resorts attract large numbers of tourist visitors. Cheap package holidays are available and people can stay in apartments and large hotel complexes. Local business people and large leisure companies provide facilities for tourists to use and enjoy. Beaches and attractions can become very busy, local services expand and involve heavy traffic in the tourist season. Sometimes large visitor numbers create environmental pressure or places become too crowded and begin to discourage tourists who look to other newer destinations for holidays.

Tourism continues to grow in world terms as people begin to earn more money from industrial jobs and have more leisure time. As countries like China and India see growth in their economies they too are developing tourist activity and seeing more and more people travelling further afield. Trends in tourism seen for many years in developed countries are now being mirrored in the developing economies.

Fig 3.22 A crowded beach in Costa del Sol, Spain

Quick Test

1. Why are some areas particularly attractive to tourists? (Use specific examples such as the Alpine ski areas, the Caribbean Islands, Africa's national parks (safaris), rainforests, spectacular scenery areas, Florida, Spain's tourist coasts and holiday islands.)

2. In what ways has tourism affected the areas you have chosen above?

What is eco-tourism?

Eco-tourism is a rapidly expanding market. As people look for new holiday ideas they may journey to increasingly exotic locations encouraged by such things as greater accessibility from cheap air fares etc. Wider knowledge of the world through media sources such as TV programmes creates a demand for access to environmentally sensitive areas so that visitor numbers once associated with popular mass tourist destinations may be finding their way to important wildlife and cultural centres. This may create new problems like those already seen in popular tourist hot spots.

Eco-tourist destinations that are under threat

- Safari holidays to Africa visit environmentally sensitive areas and may not be able to manage large numbers of visitors in what was previously an exclusive activity. New hotels encroach on national parks and animal habitats. Water supply and sewage management may cause issues.
- Whale watching trips can cause disturbance to wildlife if they are un-regulated. Scuba diving can have an impact on reefs such as the Great Barrier Reef of Australia or the Red Sea. Air boat tours in Florida cause disturbance.
- Trekking in the Himalayas puts demands on local water or wood supplies and therefore has an impact on forests in Nepal. This leads to increased pressure on the land and to conflict between tourists and farmers. Loss of forest creates major flood and soil erosion problems.
- Visits to cultural sites such as Machu Picchu or the Pyramids in Egypt turns these into tourist honey pots and eventually begins to damage the cultural heritage. People visit tombs and historic sites in large numbers and excessive footfall and even the problems caused by the effects of breathing out carbon dioxide onto the walls can affect monuments and heritage sites.

Conserving heritage sites and environmentally sensitive areas

The Lascaux Caves in France are a World Heritage Site famous for their cave paintings. Visitors are no longer allowed to visit the caves because of the damage that was caused to the priceless Stone Age art works. Instead 'New Lascaux' was built as an exact replica so that visitors can still get an impression of the original site.

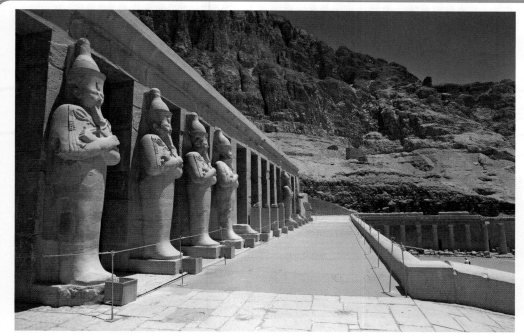

Fig 3.23 Mortuary Temple of Hatshepsut, near the Valley of the Kings, in Luxor, Egypt

At the Valley of the Kings in Egypt four hundred or more tourists visit the tombs each day, each leaving behind an ounce of moisture – about a third of a teacup – from their breath. Bright lights are needed so that visitors can see, and these raise the temperature in the tombs; these and other factors are slowly destroying the tombs and the paintings inside. Scientists who have identified this problem have developed a plan to build new visitor centres with simulations like those built at Lascaux, along with roads and flood control systems to protect this World Heritage Site from further damage.

Endangered species like orangutans, chimpanzees or mountain gorillas are now mostly found in nature reserves. Visitors may contribute to their eventual survival by providing conservation income but may equally contribute to their extinction by disturbing their increasingly threatened habitat.

Eco-tourism can be an important way of preserving the environment and ecology of an area but it needs to be managed in such a way that it is sustainable and the impact of visitors is minimised.

DID YOU KNOW?

You can calculate your tourism carbon footprint by doing some research using the Internet. This might let you plan a holiday that makes a minimum environmental impact. One search delivered the following site: www.carbonzero.co.nz.

Quick Test

1. What is eco-tourism?

2. Why do tourist developments in environmentally sensitive areas have to be carefully planned?

3. Why do theme parks and visitor attractions like the Disney Parks put pressure on the environment?

Where and why does tourism develop around the globe?

City heritage sites

Cities with major historic, cultural and entertainment functions.

Fig 3.24 New york city

Reasons for location

Barcelona – Cultural heritage, cruise liner port, architecture (Gaudi), art (Picasso Museum), lively city atmosphere at Las Ramblas, beaches and hotels, football and Olympic heritage.

Paris – Historic city centre, classic churches (Notre Dame), museums and art galleries (Louvre), Monuments (Eiffel Tower, Arc de Triomphe), night life, restaurants and bars.

Prague – Historic city (castle/palace), lively city centre, restaurants and bars, short city break weekend destination.

New York – Modern city architecture, museums and galleries, tourist hotspots (Central Park), film locations, theatre and musical district (Broadway), tourist attractions (Statue of Liberty, Time Square, Wall Street), shopping, bars and restaurants.

Environmental impact and management issues

- Cities become overcrowded, traffic conjestion, honeypots and main attractions become very busy.
- Historic buildings lose their charm – other users such as churchgoers are affected.
- Sites damaged by footfall and overuse.
- Weekend/short breaks may involve anti-social behaviour such as stag and hen parties.

National park and scenic areas

Areas with particularly attractive scenery and leisure facilities.

Reasons for location

Lake District National Park, UK – Lakeland scenery, associations with poets and writers (Wordsworth, Beatrix Potter), camping, outdoor pursuits and motor touring.

Yellowstone National Park, USA – Volcanic scenery, geysers (Old Faithful), wildlife interest (bears, wolves and bald eagles).

Florida Everglades National Park, USA – Wetland heritage area, wildlife (birds and alligators), near to Miami, Orlando, and other Florida holiday destinations (Disney, Kennedy Space Centre), Florida Keys marine coastal nature reserves (John Pennekamp Reserve).

Environmental impact and management issues

- Range of visitor pressures on popular honeypot sites like those mentioned.
- Disturbance of wildlife and nature.
- Traffic congestion.
- Florida's popularity as a mass tourist destination causes urban sprawl, water management and pollution problems in the Everglades and similar wetland environments.
- Large numbers of visitors move on to other local sites beyond the Orlando Disney complex.
- Natural heritage under threat from development.

Ski resort development

Reasons for location

Cairngorms and Grampian Ski areas, Aviemore, European Alps, American Rockies – Skiing and winter sports are developed based on snow resources in the ski season. Tourist infrastucture is built on a large scale. Transport and uplift capacity is increased to serve tourists and visitors. Olympic and World Cup events bring in extra visitors and facilities.

Environmental impact and management issues

- Impact on wildlife and nature in scenic areas.
- Large tourist complexes change the nature of remote mountain districts.
- Forests areas are cleared.
- Demand is put on local land and water resources.

Quick Test

1. Why does building in wetlands provide environmental challenges?
2. Why do major events like the World Cup or the Olympic games cause concerns about their environmental impact?
3. What benefits do tourist developments bring to an area?

Development

Development is the improvement in the standard of living in a country. This can mean many things, such as better education, access to clean water, or improved job opportunities.

Measuring development

We use indicators of development: social, economic, composite. An indicator has to be something that we can measure so that we can compare between one country and another.

Social and economic indicators of development

Social indicators	Economic indicators
• Doctors per 100,000 of the population. • Adult literacy rates. • Number of children attending secondary school. • Life expectancy.	• Average income per person. • Gross domestic product (GDP) – the value of goods and services produced by a country. • Gross national product (GNP) – how much a country earns. Includes value of goods and services involved in trade. It is measured in US$ per person.

Fig 3.25 Indicators of development

Composite indicators of development

We need to use more than one indicator to give an accurate picture so it's best to use composite indicators of development:

• Physical Quality of Life Index (PQLI) – this combines life expectancy, adult literacy rate and infant mortality rate. Each of the indicators is given a rating of between 0 and 100, with 0 = the worst and 100 = the highest.

• Human Development Index (HDI) – a social welfare index. It is a composite of educational attainment (adult literacy and years in education), life expectancy at birth and income per capita (per person).

Indicators of development can be very useful in telling us whether a country is developed or developing.

	UK	France	Ghana	Kenya
Birth rate (live births per 1000 people per year)	11	13	29	38
Death rate (deaths per 1000 people per year)	10	8	9	10
Life expectancy	79	81	59	57
GNP per person (US$)	33 800	33 600	1330	1540
Doctors per 100,000 people	230	336.7	15.2	13.9
Internet usage (% of population)	82	79.6	14.0	28

Fig 3.26 Composite indicators of development

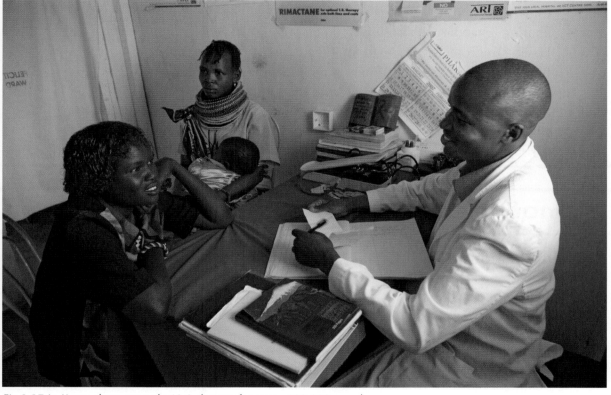

Fig 3.27 In Kenya there are only 13.9 doctors for every 100,000 people

Quick Test

1. Using the table above, which country is most developed and why?
2. What are the problems in using only one or two of the indicators listed?

The distribution of world diseases: AIDS – a case study of a world disease

AIDS is an incurable disease caused by the Human Immunodeficiency Virus (HIV). It is a global disease but 70% of all AIDS/HIV cases are in Africa, and the distribution is very uneven.

Causes of AIDS

- HIV/AIDS is spread in three main ways:
    - Sharing a needle with an infected person.
    - Having unprotected sex with an infected person.
    - Babies drinking the breast milk of an infected mother.
- HIV/AIDS can also be spread by infected blood transfusions.
- A lack of education accelerates the spread of the disease as does a lack of contraception.
- Poverty is a key factor.

Economic effects/impact of AIDS

Developing countries
- Inability of workforce to deliver in their job – high absence rates through illness impacts on production levels.
- As adults become ill, children are forced to stop their education to look after their parents and try to earn money. The result is that the next generation of African adults will be less educated, less wealthy and possibly less healthy.
- Resources are diverted away from other projects into health care and particularly into the treatment of AIDS, which means less money and less health care for people with other diseases.

Developed countries
- People die younger so they have fewer years in the economically active bracket of population composition.
- As people become ill, they cannot work, so the cycle of ill health comes into effect, impacting on the economy.
- There will be fewer taxpayers so the country produces less wealth.
- → These are all also applicable to developing countries.

Social effects/impact of AIDS

- Stigma associated with HIV/AIDS can lead to mental health problems.
- Very large number of orphans = family unit breakdown.
- Negative effect on educaton = possible rise in illiteracy rates and uneducated nation.

Strategies to reduce the spread of AIDS

Developing countries

There is no cure for AIDS but the following can help reduce the impact:

- Health education programs
- Free testing for HIV
- Distribution of free condoms
- Reduce poverty
- Reduction in malnutrition

Developed countries

- Widespread availability of ARV (antiretroviral) drugs.
- Drugs to stop the disease passing from pregnant mothers to their babies.

> **EXAM TIP**
> Link the impact to the development of a case study country.

How effective are the controls for AIDS

The controls are not very effective, for the following reasons:

- There are not enough drugs or medication for everyone. Only 5% of babies who need to be treated actually receive the drugs.
- Poverty – countries cannot afford to buy the drugs and administer them.
- There are not enough trained staff to administer treatments.
- Many people are in denial or ignorant of the spread of disease.
- High illiteracy rates limit the success of education programs.

To some extent the controls work. Drugs allow children to remain well enough to receive an education (but they can struggle to keep up). Life expectancy increases, which allows family to remain together longer and reduces the number of children orphaned.

Quick Test

1. Explain the causes of AIDS
2. What are the consequences of the disease on the economy of a country?
3. How can the impact of AIDS be reduced?

Managing disease in developing countries

Diseases such as cholera, malaria, kwashiorkor and pneumonia are more prevalent in developing countries. You must know the causes, effects and strategies to manage **one disease** in detail, from the list above.

Case study material – malaria

Malaria is a disease that is *endemic* in many countries – this means it is always present. Those who survive develop a limited measure of immunity in adulthood. They can however be re-infected, suffer from recurrent and violent bouts of fever and are severely anaemic.

Malaria is an infectious disease and is found mainly in the world's poorest tropical areas, such as Africa, South America and South-East Asia but apart from hot and cold deserts and high altitudes, mosquitoes have a worldwide distribution.

How malaria spreads

Malaria is a mosquito-borne, potentially fatal, blood disease. It is caused by a parasite that is transmitted to human and animal hosts by the *Anopheles* mosquito.

1. Infected mosquito bites a human.

2. The parasite is in the liver within 30 minutes.

3. The parasite multiplies rapidly in the liver. Parasites can lie dormant in the liver for years before being activated.

4. The parasite enters the blood stream and attaches to red blood cells; it multiplies further.

5. Infected red blood cells burst, infecting other blood cells.

6. The cycles repeats, reducing the oxygen in the body and causing fever. The cycle corresponds to the fever and chills experienced by someone who is sick with malaria.

7. After it has been released a dormant version of malaria stays in the blood stream. If an uninfected mosquito bites this person it will ingest the parasite and go on to infect someone else.

The impact of malaria

Malaria holds back development. In Thailand it costs the people nine times their daily income on drug treatments to control the disease. A bout of illness requires at least five days off work. The economy suffers as a result. Therefore there is not enough money to spend on education, which is crucial to the development of any country.

Methods used to control the spread of malaria

ABCDE!

A – be AWARE of the risk

B – avoid mosquito BITES

C – take your CHEMOPROPHYLAXIS (medication to help prevent malaria)

D – DIAGNOSE quickly

E – if more than 24 hours from medical attention, take a course of EMERGENCY stand-by treatment.

Other controls include work done by charities such as the Roll Back Malaria Campaign and the Bill & Melinda Gates Foundation. They support research and development for more effective treatment and spend time educating local people about what they can do. They believe that prevention is better than cure.

Quick Test

Using the Internet, research how effective these measures are and complete the table.

Preventative method	Effectiveness
Bed nets	
Window and door screens	
Insecticides	
Draining marshes and swamps (where mosquitoes easily breed)	
The latest anti-malarial drug artemisinin	A potential treatment: so far there has been little evidence of the parasite developing resistance to the drug, which is very positive, but there were some concerns about resistance in Indonesia a couple of years ago, so only time will tell.

Managing disease in developed countries

Diseases such as heart disease, cancer and asthma are more prevalent in developed countries. You must know the causes, effects and strategies to manage one of these diseases in detail.

Case study material – heart disease

Fig 3.28 Doctor taking patient's blood pressure

Effects and consequences

- Inability to work.
- Lower life expectancy.
- Increased medical/health costs – operations, re-enforced beds for patients with obesity.

Strategies to manage the spread of heart disease

- Government policies, e.g. '5 A Day' the smoking ban and raising the age for purchasing cigarettes.
- More advanced medical care allows early diagnosis – prevention is better than cure.
- Advertising campaigns that encourage people to take more exercise, which helps prevent heart disease.
- Medical intervention – new drugs, clot removal and strengthening the arteries help control the disease.

Fig 3.29 People are encouraged to eat 5 different pieces of fruit and veg a day

Control methods

Many of the controls are unsuccessful:

- Despite health warnings, people continue to smoke and drink alcohol at unhealthy levels.

- People are not taking enough exercise and obesity levels are at their highest in the UK, so advertising campaigns do not appear to be working.

- Technology and gaming are the most popular pastimes for young people, which means they are not taking enough regular exercise and are key candidates for future heart disease.

Fig 3.30 Despite warnings, poor diet and lack of exercise is common

Linking development and health

Question: How can levels of development help to reduce global health issues?

Answer: Increased development = better economy = more money available for health resources, better education, increased sanitation. This will help reduce disease and enable health care for illnesses.

Quick Test

1. For AIDS, heart disease, or malaria, what are the causes?
2. For a disease you have studied, what are the main consequences?
3. How effective are the controls?

Glossary

Abrasion
Erosion caused by the rubbing and scouring effect of material carried by rivers, glaciers, waves and wind.

AIDS
A disease of the human immune system caused by infection with human immunodeficiency virus (HIV).

Air Masses
Stationary air that takes on the characteristics of the region it is above.

Air Stream
Movement of air from these air masses.

Altitude
The height of the Earth's surface.

Amazonia
A large area of Brazil centred on the Amazon River and its tributaries. It is also called the Amazon River Basin.

Arête
A narrow, knife-edged ridge formed by glacial erosion when two adjacent corries erode back to back.

ARV drugs
Antiretroviral drugs used in the treatment of HIV infection.

Aspect
Direction in which a slope, building or settlement faces.

Brown field site
Land previously used for industrial purposes.

Butler Model
A model of tourism development over time showing the rise, development, decline and rejuvenation of tourism in an area.

Choropleth map
A thematic map in which areas are shaded or patterned in proportion to the measurement of the statistical variable being displayed on the map, such as population density or per-capita income.

Conurbation
A conurbation is formed when cities and towns expand sufficiently that their urban areas join up with each other.

Corrie
An armchair-shaped hollow caused by glacial erosion.

Deforestation
The cutting down of trees and clearing of forests.

Deposition
The process whereby eroded material is left behind on the landscape by such things as glaciers, rivers, the wind or the sea.

El Nino
A band of anomalously warm ocean water temperatures that occasionally develops off the western coast of South America and can cause climatic changes across the Pacific Ocean.

Endemic diseases
When a **disease** is prevalent in an area over long periods of time, it is considered to be **endemic** in that area.

Enhanced greenhouse effect
An increase in the natural process of the greenhouse effect, brought about by human activities like **burning fossil fuels** and **deforestation**, whereby greenhouse gases such as carbon dioxide, methane, chlorofluorocarbons and nitrous oxide are being released into the atmosphere at a far greater rate than would occur through natural processes and thus their concentrations are increasing.

Erosion
The wearing away of the landscape by river, glacial and marine processes such as abrasion, hydraulic action and attrition.

Evapotranspiraton
Loss of water from plants and the Earth's surface.

Favelas
A Brazilian term for an informal shanty-type settlement.

Freeze-thaw weathering
A process of physical weathering by which rock disintegrates, caused by water in cracks repeatedly freezing and thawing.

Gentrification
The process of renewing and rebuilding an area due to the influx of more affluent residents.

Glacier
A river of ice.

Global warming
An increase in the average temperature of Earth's atmosphere and oceans.

Green belt
An area of land around a large urban area where development is severely restricted.

Greenhouse gases
Gases in the atmosphere that absorb and emit radiation, e.g. carbon dioxide, water vapour, methane.

Hanging valley
A tributary valley left high above the main valley as its glacier was unable to erode as deeply as the glacier in the main valley.

Human development index
A composite statistic of life expectancy, education, and income indices used to rank countries according to their level of development.

Impermeable
A property, for example in rock layers, that does not allow water to pass through the structure.

Permeable structures allow the passage of water. Porous rocks have numbers of interlinking air spaces that soak up water like a sponge.

Indicators of development
Statistics/figures used to determine how developed a country is. Classified as social, economic or composite indicators.

Karst scenery
Areas of mainly carboniferous limestone affected by chemical weathering by acidic rainfall.

Latitude
Lines running parallel to the Equator.

Levees
Naturally formed embankments found along the sides of rivers in their middle and lower courses.

Longshore drift
The movement of sediment along the coastline, caused by wave transportation.

Malaria
An intermittent and remittent fever caused by a parasite that invades the red blood cells.

Meanders
Naturally occurring bends in rivers created by turbulent corkscrewing river action.

Migration
The movement of people either within a country or between countries, either voluntary or forced.

Misfit stream
A stream or river in a glaciated valley that is too small to have eroded the valley in which it flows.

Natural disaster
A major adverse event resulting from natural processes of the Earth; examples include floods, volcanic eruptions, earthquakes, tsunamis.

Névé
Old, compacted snow.

Glossary

Pedestrianisation
To convert a street into a pedestrian walkway or mall.

Physical quality of life index
An attempt to measure the quality of life or well-being of a country. The value is the average of three statistics: basic literacy rate, infant mortality, and life expectancy at age one, all equally weighted on a 0 to 100 scale.

Plucking
A process of glacial erosion by which ice freezes onto weathered rock and as it moves, pulls pieces of rock with it.

Pyramidal peak
A triangular shaped mountain formed by three or more corries erode back to back.

Ranching
A type of farming that uses large areas of land to raise cattle, sheep and other livestock. The land is predominantly used for grazing and large numbers of livestock will be involved.

Regeneration
Improving an area.

Relief
The shape of the Earth's surface.

Ribbon lake
A long narrow lake found on the floor of a glaciated valley.

Rural-urban fringe
A zone of transition between the built-up area and the countryside where there is often competition for land use.

Rural-urban migration
Movement of people from the countryside to cities.

Scarp
A steep slope often with a cliff that runs across the landscape and relates to erosion and exposure of underlying rock layers or to processes like faulting that involves uplift of the land.

Self-help schemes
Where groups of people, especially in developing countries, are encouraged to build or improve their own homes using materials provided by the local authority.

Solar radiation
Heat from the sun.

Sustainability
Land use systems that can be continued into the future without short, mid-term, or permanent damage to the environment and its ecosystems.

Tourism
A global industry that involves short medium and long-stay journeys to areas beyond home.

Transect
A series of zones that transition from sparse rural farmhouses to the dense urban core.

Transition zone
An area of change within a city where the boundaries between zones is blurred (e.g. the move from the C.B.D. to the inner city).

Transportation
The movement of materials by agents of erosion such as running water, glaciers, the wind and the sea.

Truncated spur
A former interlocking spur in a pre-glacial V-shaped valley that had its end removed by a glacier.

U-shaped valley
A wide valley with steep sides and a flat floor formed by glacial erosion.

V-shaped valley
A narrow, steep-sided valley formed by the rapid vertical erosion of a river.

Answers

Britain's Weather, page 9

1. Tropical maritime and polar maritime air masses.

2. Cold air because it is more dense.

3. A front is where two air masses meet e.g. warm Tm and cold Pm air.

4. An occluded front.

5. Clockwise.

The passage of a depression over Britain, page 13

1. West to East.

2. Short heavy burst of rain, wind direction changes (backs around), temperatures fall in the cold sector.

3. Anticyclone.

4. Cold, frosty, still air conditions, frost with very cold nights and cold sunny days.

Weather plots activity, page 13

1.
   - Wind SW 25 kts, –5 degrees, full cloud cover (8 oktas)
   - Wind NW 5 kts, –2 degrees, snow showers, cloud cover 4 oktas
   - Wind E 1–2 kts, 20 degrees, thunder storms, cloud cover 6 oktas

2. (a)   (b)   (c)

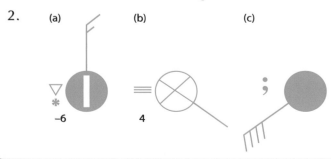

3. a. a. Wind NW 15 kts, -2 degrees, 8 oktas

    b. Wind 5 kts SSW, 3 degrees, 2 oktas

    e. Wind NW 25 kts, 2 degrees, 8 oktas

    g. Wind W 20 kts, 6 degrees, hail showers, 4 oktas

    b. Wind blowing at 25 kts from the SW raining, 6 degrees, full cloud cover. There is a warm front passing over and this brings persistent rain as the warm air in the system is forced to rise over the cold air in front of it.

Factors affecting climate and weather in the UK, page 15

1. Winds are strongest where the isobars (lines of equal air pressure) are close together and lighter where they are further apart as in a high pressure system or anticyclone.

2. Latitude, relief/altitude, aspect and distance from the sea.

3. You should have marked on your map the following air streams: Polar maritime (Pm), Tropical maritime (Tm), Tropical continental (Tc), Arctic maritime (Am) and Polar continental (Pc).

4. Places at the Equator are warmer than the Poles because the sun is directly overhead whereas at the Poles the sun strikes the Earth at a lower angle and has to heat up a greater area due to the curvature of the Earth.

River landscapes, page 17

1. Rivers erode the landscape using hydraulic action, corrasion, attrition and corrosion and solution.

2. Hydraulic action is the moving river water forcing air in and out of rock cracks, causing them to expand and contract, breaking off bits of the bedrock.

3. Corrasion is the grinding effect produced by the sediment the river carries scraping over the surface. Attrition is when fragments of rock are broken in the flow by rock-to-rock contact. Solution is when soluble rock components dissolve in the river water.

The formation of river features, page 19

1. Using processes like hydraulic action and corrasion the river erodes the softer rock and undercuts the hard rock of the river bed.

2. An oxbow lake is a meander that has been abandoned by the river when it cuts through the meander neck.

3. Levees are formed when the river breaks over the top of its banks as it does it deposits silt to for a raised bank.

4. **Exam-style question**: Base your sketch on Fig 1.15. You should mention the following things: differences in rock type and hardness; river erosion, e.g. hydraulic action and corrosion; undercutting and the formation of the plunge pool; collapse of the rock ledge. Marks can be gained by discussing the formation of the gorge. Annotations on the sketch can be used as an alternative to written text to gain some of the marks above.

5. **Exam-style question**: Draw a series of diagrams based on the meander diagrams above, explain how the river erodes its banks using hydraulic action and corrasion, show how the river erodes the outside of the bends at the attack points, explain how the river eventually breaks through and abandons the old meander to form an ox-bow lake

Rivers on OS maps, pages 20–21

1. a. The River Allt Creag an Leth-choin rises at 1050 metres and flows NE to Coire an Lochan. At 981030 it turns due south to a junction with a tributary at 980062. The river is in its upper course because of the steep relief. It flows through a steep sided gorge at 985067, again typical of the upper course. It has many small meanders along its course (square 9806). Having turned in a westerly direction at 985091 it enters Loch Morlich through a small delta at 970092.

   b. 964026: U-shaped valley
      981028: corrie and lochan
      988035: arête
      004026: hanging valley

2. a. There are many tourist related activities shown on the map, for example the ski area 995054 is an important part of the local economy. It provides many jobs managing the slopes as well as in the shops in Aviemore 893118. The National Mountaineering Training Centre 986093 and the Cairngorm corries 985026 show

that mountaineering provides similar income to local people. Skiing and mountaineering can have an environmental impact, for example, the funicular railway and the ski tows create a visual intrusion. Visitors may be attracted to honeypots such as the Loch Morlich water sports centre 972098; this may cause overcrowding and disturbance to wildlife. Visitors to the Glenmore Forest Park 9710 may cause damage to trees by lighting fires, or may disturb wildlife with dogs or mountain bike activities.

b. Corries form on cold north facing slopes in hollows where snow collected during the ice age. As it accumulated it turned to glacier ice and began to slide downhill due to gravity. The ice eroded the hollow deeper and deeper using plucking. Where the ice tore away the bedrock it was wrapped around as it moved and by abrasion using rock fragments like sandpaper to wear away the rock. After the Ice Age the deep armchair shaped hollow was left and rainwater trapped in its bottom formed the lochan called a tarn.

3. a. A: forest track
   B: river
   C: forest edge
   D: ski area
   E: Fiacaill a' Coire Cais

   b. This is a question which calls for an opinion and is designed to get you to think about the issue and come to your own conclusion. **Did you justify your opinion with facts?**

4. a. There are a wide range of leisure and tourist features on the map. Skiing is found at 994054, water sports at Lock Morlich 971098. The forest is used for mountain biking with a cycle track at 978080. The camping ground and youth hostel in 9709 provide accommodation.

   b. Leisure and tourism are important to the local economy as tourists spend money in the shops and hotels in Aviemore. Visitors create employment for local people and the ski industry keeps the economy going in the winter. These jobs help to prevent our migration from this mountainous area and maintain the population of the area. Many people can get jobs in outdoor activities such as at the National Outdoor Training Centre 985093. Skilled jobs are created working for bodies like the National Park Authority as a conservationist and these attract a higher rate of pay.

Limestone scenery, page 25

Exam-style question
(i) 876643 – caves; 893658 – swallow hole; 900647 – limestone pavement; 914640 – gorge.

(ii) Answers should include ideas such as acidic rainwater (carbonic acid) dissolving limestone beds and joints to open them up. Streams disappear down open joints. Words like clints and grykes should be included. Underground caves are formed by water eroding and dissolving the limestone to create large underground spaces. Waterfalls and gorges are explained by cave roof collapse.

Quick Test

1. It is acidic and dissolves the limestone.

2. Clints and grykes: acid rain opens up the joints on the surface and leaves crevices and upstanding blocks. Swallow holes: river water enters a joint and opens it up by dissolving the limestone so the river works its way underground following the joints and bedding planes.

3. It would show as bare rocky areas.

4. They are formed by dripping water leaving behind deposits of the mineral calcite on the floor and ceiling of the cave.

Land use and land use conflict in limestone areas, page 29

1. Loud noises will drive animals and birds away; breeding birds do not like disturbance; heavy vehicles and blasting produce vibrations; dust damages habitats.

2. Visitors will be put off by heavy road traffic and will not return; noise and dust spoil the area for visitors; restrictions on where people can walk spoils their enjoyment.

3. They are usually very effective: quarrying continues to provide local jobs and income; nature and wildlife are protected; visitors are less aware of the noise and disruption caused by quarrying; local people continue to benefit from tourist incomes and related jobs.

Glaciation, page 31

1. Plucking and Abrasion.

2. Erosion, Transportation and Deposition.

Answers

Landforms of erosion, page 33

1. **Plucking** – Ice freezes onto rock and when the ice moves it pulls a piece of rock away (the tweezer effect)
   Abrasion- pieces of rock carried by the ice scrape at the surrounding rock and erode it away (the sandpaper effect)
2. Corrie, arête, pyramidal peak, U-shaped valley, ribbon lake, misfit stream, hanging valley e.g. in The Cairngorms Coire Cas (Corrie), Loch Avon (ribbon lake), Glen Avon (U-shaped valley).

Case study – Cairngorm National Park, page 35

1. Snow collects in north facing hollows, erosion as glacier moves downhill, abrasion deepens the hollow, plucking steepens the back wall. When the ice melts, a tarn or corrie loch may be present.

2. Increased tourism conflicts with conservations who want to protect the landscape. Tourism conflicts with locals as there can be increased litter, traffic congestion at peak periods and footpath erosion in popular walking areas leaving unsightly scarring on the landscape. Farming activities are often in conflict with walkers' rights of access, walkers leaving gates open and dogs chasing sheep.

3. Park Rangers are employed to prevent problems developing. Strict planning permission for developments is in place. Visitor centre staff aim to educate visitors about looking after National Parks. Voluntary bodies such as the National Trust protect areas by organising litter picks, buying land and buildings and maintaining walls and footpaths.

The coast – erosion, page 39

1. The fetch (the distance over which the wave travels), the windspeed and the depth of the water.

2. Constructive waves have a strong swash and a weak backwash and so build up a beach. Destructive waves have a weak swash and a powerful backwash which erode the beach.

3. This is where the waves have cut away at the base of a cliff.

The coast – transportation and deposition, page 41

1. The fetch is the distance over which the wave travels.

2. If the movement of a wave up the beach (the swash) is stronger than the return flow of the wave (the backwash) the wave is likely to be a constructive wave. If the opposite is true the wave will probably have a destructive effect on the beach.

3. Hydraulic action, attrition, corrosion and corrosion.

4. The angle at which the waves approach the coastline is determined by the wind direction. Therefore the waves usually approach at an angle. As the swash of a wave washes up a beach it carries material up in the same direction the wave has approached from. The backwash, however, pulls the material back down to the sea at right angles to the water under the influence of gravity. This means sand and other materials such as shingle are moved in a zig-zag path along the coast.

Coastal land uses, page 43

1. Army firing ranges, Nature trails, the South West Coastal path, an Animal Sanctuary, Tourist resort, an Adventure farm, cycleways and parking.

2. Increased erosion, increased pollution, increased industrial and tourist development, increased tourism, reduced sediment supply and a possible increase in sea-level.

Population distribution, page 47

1. Flat land, fertile soils and plenty of natural resources.

2. Lack of precipitation, steep slopes and poor soils.

3. Southern Bangladesh – flat, fertile flood plain with plenty of precipitation and warmth.

4. Northern Nepal – steep slopes, poor access and thin soils.

Answers

World population growth, page 49

1. Birth rate – the number of live births per 1000 people per year. Death rate – the number of deaths per 1000 people per year. Natural increase – taking the death rate from the birth rate gives an indication of how much the population is increasing each year per thousand of the population.

2. Migration.

3. Improved medical care – vaccination, hospitals, doctors, new drugs and scientific advances. Improved sanitation and access to clean water.

4. Developing countries: no birth control or family planning. Many children are needed to help work on the land. Developed countries: increased desire for material possessions such as cars, holidays and less desire for a large family. An increased number of women having careers and either starting a family later in life or choosing not to have children.

Population structures in developed and developing countries, page 51

1. A population pyramid.

2. High birth rate.

3. High death rate.

How does the population change over time, page 53

1. Stage 1: slow population increase, high fluctuating birth and death rates. Stage 2: early expanding, high birth rates and declining death rates. Stage 3: late expanding, declining death rates, low death rates. Stage 4: steady population, low, fluctuating birth and death rates.

2. Older people need more health care and there is a greater need for public services such as social services and hospitals as well as care/retirement homes. There is increased taxation of the working population to fund the above. A smaller young population means that this will be an increasing strain on the country's finances.

3. Overcrowding, poverty, unemployment, inadequate housing, education and health care services. Lack of formal employment, leading to informal sector jobs, increased crime rates. Lack of basic infrastructure such as clean water and waste disposal.

Urban land use zones, page 56

1. A conurbation is a large, continuous built-up area created by towns and cities expanding and growing together.

2. Suburbs: Semi-detached and detached housing, outer-city council estates with flats, high rise and mixed housing. Inner city: High-rise flats, mixture of old and newer buildings, new houses of mixed type, redevelopment occurring. C.B.D.: Department shops, large offices, main railway and bus stations, many churches, pubs, clubs and cinemas and the town hall.

Recent developments or changes in a developing world city, page 59

The authorities sometimes improve sanitation. Installation of clean water. Improving the quality of housing. Organising rubbish collection. Giving squatters legal ownership of land. Planning new settlements e.g. Barra. Self help schemes. Provision of electricity.

Recent developments or changes in a developed world city, page 61

1. Possible answers include: Decline of industry, new housing, new entertainment areas such as cinemas, improved public transport, gentrification of the area.

2. Possible answers include: Positive changes: pedestrianisation to relieve traffic congestion, provide a safer environment and to reduce pollution; small independent shops replaced with larger chain stores because of high costs in city centres; covered shopping malls built to protect customers from weather. Negative changes: shop closure caused by competition from out of town developments etc.

Modern factors affecting farming, page 65

1. CAP is the the Common Agricultural Policy.

2. Using GM crops may affect the natural environment by cross breeding with existing plants. GM crops cannot be grown on or near organic farms. GM crops may be considered unsafe or may be lower priced than non GM crops and this is seen as unfair if a country does not allow its farmers to use GM seeds.

3. By producing biofuels or alternative energy to reduce our national carbon footprint, and by using environmentally sensitive methods such as preserving hedgerows and not spraying wild flower meadows.

4. Infected animals are slaughtered and disposed of, farms are quarantined.

Brazil developing the Amazon, page 67

1. Matto Grosso.

2. North-East Brazil (Sertao).

Sustainable development in Brazil, page 69

1. Plantations are large scale farms that produce industrial raw materials such as rubber, palm oil, cotton, mass consumption fruit, nuts, coffee and tea.

2. Blood diamonds are gems produced in rebel held areas sold on the black market and are not produced by legitimate companies or by legitimate governments from their mines. They are used to fund terrorism and to exploit natural resources that should benefit the whole country.

3. This is an important way to be sure that endangered species are not exploited and driven to extinction.

4. Fair trade provides a higher income for small scale farmers and ensures that they can farm sustainably and support their families on a fair living wage.

What is climate change?, page 73

1. Changes in the amount of energy given out by the sun over time, Volcanic Dust acts as a blanket shielding the Earth from incoming solar radiation and leads to a decrease in temperature, changes in the movement of the earth's angle of tilt, its orbit around the sun and the gravitational pull of the sun and the moon all change the amount of energy the earth receives from the sun, therefore influencing climatic temperature, Changing oceanic circulation eg: El Nino/la nina

2. Humans can increase the amount of greenhouse gases in the Atmosphere. Climate change is added to by increased deforestation as a lack of trees means more CO_2 as photosynthesis is reduced, burning of fossil fuels releases more CO_2 into the atmosphere, more methane caused by increased demand for more rice padi fields and cows for meat, and increased use of vehicles on the roads leads to more nitrous oxides.

Consequences of climate change, page 75

1. To reduce the effects of climate change we should be reducing our use of fossil fuels, increasing recycling, switching off lights when not in use to reduce use of electricity, cycling or walking instead of driving. Or any other relevant point.

2. Evidence for climate change includes retreat of glaciers and ice caps, changes in biodiversity, climate records such as increased temperatures on a global scale and reduction in sea ice limits.

Equatorial versus tundra environments, page 77

1. Annual precipitation is always over 2000 mm so there is plenty of moisture and average temperatures are over 26 C.

2. Annual precipitation is 250 mm or less.

3. Infertile soils.

4. Equatorial environments are found in lowland areas within 10 degrees of the Equator. Tundra environments are found are found north of the Arctic Circle (66½ degrees N).

5. Equatorial environments provide a hot and wet climate all year round. This has led to the establishment of dense rainforest with evergreen trees of varying height. Tundra environments are cold and harsh for most of the year, so it is treeless and characterised by grasses, flowers, mosses and lichens which are hardy and close to the ground.

Misuse of equatorial rainforests, page 79

1. The removal of trees.

2. Loss of an invaluable resource of raw materials for medical drugs.

3. The rainforests are so dense that they are very difficult to patrol.

4. Four causes of deforestation: ranching, mining activities, logging and hydro-electric power (HEP) schemes.

Answers

Misuse of the Tundra, page 81

1. Two activities threatening the tundra are the oil industry and mining activities.

2. Three positive effects of development in equatorial and tundra environments are the creation of jobs, increased incomes and improved infrastructure, i.e. roads.

Environmental hazards case study: Bangladesh, page 85

1. Hazard maps show the likely effects of natural disasters and hazards such as blast zones from volcanoes or areas liable to flooding along a river valley. They are used to warn where people are likely to need to be evacuated from or where protection schemes are required.

2. A typhoon is a tropical cyclone (hurricane) in the South China Seas.

3. Annotations from the list on page 83 should be used to create a list of the causes and effects of flooding in Bangladesh. E.g. Causes – Heavy monsoon, snowfall on the Himalayas produces melt water that causes flooding lower down the river basin, Forest clearance in Nepal, Bhutan and the Himalayas increase flooding and flood risks Effects – Thousands of people die each year, millions of houses are flooded affecting millions of people.

Trade, page 87

1. Imports – buy goods they need from other countries. Exports – sell to other countries goods they produce.

2. The balance of trade is the difference between a country's imports and exports.

3. Developing countries often have a trade deficit as they mainly export primary goods or raw materials which earn them less than the secondary or manufactured goods they import.

4. Interdependence describes the trading relationship between developed and developing countries. In order to survive and earn an income, developing countries rely on developed countries buying their primary goods or raw materials. However, if the developing countries did not provide the developed countries with the raw materials they could not process them and turn them into manufactured goods and so in turn they would not survive or earn an income.

Globalisation, page 89

1. Lower labour costs, higher labour availability and better communication.

2. No tariffs (import tax), free movement of labour.

3. The profits of the TNC go back to the developed country, lack of respect for the environment leading to pollution etc.

The developing world fights back, page 91

1. Trade that guarantees a good price for produce.

2. At least 20%

What is global tourism?, page 93

1. Tourism provides many jobs, income to a wide range of people and tax revenues for governments.

2. It may lead to overcrowding as the area becomes too popular. People may become bored with the area and move on to new locations.

3. This would ensure the long term decline of an area and the loss of its income. The area would become unattractive and go into more major decline.

What impact does tourism have on an area?, page 95

Answers will vary depending on which area has been chosen.

Answers

What is eco-tourism?, page 97

1. Eco-tourism is when people visit areas known for their special conservation value, heritage or unspoiled natural environment.

2. Without careful planning, development will not take place sustainably and tourism will spoil the resource it is exploiting.

3. Large scale leisure developments in areas like Florida put heavy demand on natural resources such as land and water supplies due to the large numbers of people involved.

Where and why does tourism develop around the globe?, page 99

1. Wetlands need to be drained to build on them and this alters them and damages the environment. Extracting water resources compromises the wetland environment. Wetlands are sensitive to pollution.

2. They often involve major building works which have a high carbon footprint and may exploit natural environments for stadia and other infrastructure such as roads.

3. Tourism provides jobs and income, for example construction jobs and service industry jobs. This injects large amounts of cash into the local economy. Tourism provides tax revenues.

Development, page 101

1. France – longest life expectancy, good healthcare, high level of income and wealth in the country, low death rate.

2. Single indicators don't give an overall picture. You need a combination of both social and economic indicators to work out whether or not a country is developed.

The distribution of world diseases:
AIDS – a case study of a world disease,
page 103

1. AIDS/HIV can be spread by sharing a needle with an infected person, having unprotected sex with an infected person, babies drinking the breast milk of an infected mother and HIV/AIDS can also be spread by infected blood transfusions.

2. If someone becomes ill, they cannot work so production levels will fall, As adults become ill, children are forced to stop their education to look after their parents and try to earn money. The result is that the next generation of African adults will be less educated less wealthy and possibly less healthy. Resources are diverted away from other projects into health care and particularly into the treatment of AIDS which means less money and less health care for people with other diseases.

3. There is no cure for AIDS but health education can help reduce the impact. So too can free testing for HIV, the distribution of free condoms and use of ARV drugs.

Managing disease in developed countries,
page 107

1. AIDS can be caused by sharing a needle with an infected person, having unprotected sex with an infected person, babies drinking the breast milk of an infected mother and can be spread by infected blood transfusions. Heart disease can be caused by a lack of exercise, overeating/drinking, lifestyle/stress, eating foods high in fat. Malaria is caused by a parasite that is transmitted to human and animal hosts by the Anopheles mosquito.

2. Sample answer. Consequences of AIDS in Kenya are: loss of workforce; it hinders development, leading to fewer jobs; costs of hospital treatment increase; less wealth in country overall; death rate increases; emotional impact on relatives and friends.

3. Controls of AIDS are limited: drugs are available but there are not enough trained staff in developing countries; many isolated rural areas are difficult to reach so people are not aware of controls; many people not aware they have the disease so it is passed on in ignorance; testing facilities are poor, which can lead to incorrect results; some people try to avoid being tested; some drugs are too expensive; education campaigns difficult because of high levels of illiteracy and different dialects and languages.